THE RAIL ENTHUSIAST'S
QUIZ BOOK

THE RAIL ENTHUSIAST'S QUIZ BOOK

OVER 1,000 BAFFLING QUESTIONS

HOWARD JOHNSTON

ARCTURUS

Published by Arcturus Publishing Limited
For Bookmart Limited
Registered Number 2372865
Trading as Bookmart Limited
Desford Road
Enderby
Leicester
LE9 5AD

This edition published 1996

Printed and bound in Great Britain

ISBN1 900032 16 3

CONTENTS

Introduction
Page 6

Railway Facts and Figures
Page 8

Geography and Engineering
Page 23

Terminology
Page 34

Steam Locomotives
Page 45

Diesel and Electric Locomotives
Page 75

Match the Name
Page 93

Foreign Railways
Page 101

Preservation
Page 107

The Final Word
Page 113

The Answers
Page 117

Introduction

A TRIP on a Eurostar service through the Channel Tunnel confirms it — railways are fascinating.

In the 1990s, speed and luxury are an experience to be treasured. As we embark upon a high-tech adventure, it is easy to understand how enthusiasts have always enjoyed the freedom of a train trip.

Railway enthusiasts have an insatiable appetite for information, judging by the vast array of magazines on the newsagent's shelf. The hobby bridges the age gap, with just as many young people showing interest in the steam age as the modern era.

There have always been useful spin-offs from being a railway enthusiast — such as having a detailed knowledge of British geography, all generated from travel.

There is also the less important — you can outshine anyone in a pub quiz by being able to rattle off the names of most countries and states of the Commonwealth (if you are well-read on London Midland matters), place names in the West Country (Southern), famous country piles (Western), 1930s horse race winners and football teams, (Eastern) or characters from Sir Walter Scott novels (Scotland)!

More people are railway enthusiasts than you might believe. Mention an A4 or a 'Duchess', and you would be surprised how many unlikely people can strike up a conversation about their youthful recollections. The same applies to modern motive power — how many Class 86 or 'Deltic' regimental names can *you* recite?

The 1,000-plus questions in this book are designed to cater for this diverse audience. They are a mixed bag, taking readers from the birth of railways through to the latest designs of diesel and electric locomotives They are primarily intended to entertain, but on occasions intended will certainly task the old grey matter.

They are sub-divided into specific chapters dealing with records and achievements, technical aspects, terminology, steam, diesel and electric traction, and preservation.

Depending on your age or depth of knowledge, you are

bound to find some of the chapters easier than others. They inevitably reflect my personal interest in the out-of-the-ordinary, and I do not need to apologise that the gaps in my own knowledge have been unashamedly filled by reference to many books in my library — I suggest that you do the same.

The questions on locomotives are inevitably the most entertaining because of their mass interest, and their vast number of achievements over many years.

Most questions simply require a generous application of general knowledge and sound common sense. If you have a couple of Ian Allan ABCs or Platform Five Combined Volumes in your possession, a large number of answers to locomotive questions will quickly fall into your lap. A couple of good atlases, ancient and modern, will make life easier.

The chapters covering abbreviations and anagrams may prove a little more taxing. If all else fails... you can always resort to the answers pages at the back end of the book. Whatever happens, you can increase you knowledge and impress fellow enthusiasts with your improved mastery of the subject.

I have tried extremely hard not to duplicate any of the questions, but even in this modest book, it is almost inevitable that one or two might be repeated or overlap. Also, because I am not infallible, you might dispute an answer or two. If you do and prove me wrong, please accept my apologies in advance.

Most of the photographs are my own, but my thanks also go to long-standing friends and fellow enthusiasts Neil Pulling and Sandy Thompson for filling in a few of the gaps.

To many people, railways represent a lifetime's passion. Enjoy your hobby!

Howard Johnston
Huntingdon
Autumn 1996

CHAPTER ONE

Railway Facts and Figures

Section 1:
True or False?

PICTURE QUESTION: This famous station frontage is now part of a supermarket — where?

Are these statements true or false?

1. Ystrad Mynach is the last-listed station in the national timetable.

2. The last-built Class 60 is named *Charles Frederick Brush*.

3. The last Class 40-hauled passenger train on BR took place in 1988.

4. Bogston is a station on the Glasgow 'North Clydeside' route.

5. BR adopted the 'Barbed Wire' corporate logo in 1964.

6. Eccles Road station is in the Manchester suburbs.

7. Electric-train heat Class 56s are numbered 56101-35.

8. There was once a Class B1 4-6-0 named after the antelope *Waterbuck*.

9. The Keighley & Worth Valley Railway was reopened in 1968.

10. Sleaford has North, South, East and West junctions.

11. LMS 'Duchess' No. 46239 was named *City of Preston*.

12. British Rail's engineering works were privatised in 1989.

13. There was once a signal cabin named Box Signal Box.

14. There was once a signalbox named Louth South.

15. 'Baby Deltic' diesels worked Edinburgh suburban services.

Section 2
True or False?

PICTURE QUESTION: The 'Jolly Fisherman' was created by a pre-Grouping railway company to market a seaside resort. Which company, which location?

Are the following true or false?

1. BR abandoned the 'slip coach' on passenger trains in 1960.
2. Aberdeen has a freight yard called Charing Cross.
3. There are two stations at Thorne in South Yorkshire — Thorne North and West.
4. The Class 60 freight locomotive made its debut run in 1989.
5. Blackpool has three railway stations called North, South and Pleasure Beach.
6. Large numbers of BR locomotives were scrapped during the 1980s at Val Berry's scrapyard at Leicester.
7. Nafferton is a station on the Hull-Scarborough line.
8. Class 73 locomotive No. 73901 was originally No. E6001.
9. Downham Market is an intermediate station on the Ipswich-Cambridge line.
10. Flatwick is a station on the St Pancras-Bedford line.
11. The Government first published its Nationalisation proposals in 1945.
12. 'Britannia' Pacific No. 70047 was named *Solway Firth*.
13. St Pancras station was opened in 1868.
14. Bogle is a station on the Par-Newquay line.
15. The 24-hour timetable was adopted by BR in 1964.

Section 3:
Important dates

PICTURE QUESTION: This famous structure was opened in 1890. What is it?

1. When were Britain's railways nationalised?

2. In which year was the Beeching Report published?

3. BR's last steam locomotive was completed in 1960. At which works?

4. In which month and year was the Carlisle-Edinburgh 'Waverley' route closed?

5. What was the date of the last run of Class 55 'Deltics on BR?

6. Network SouthEast was launched in which year?

7. In which year did Isambard Kingdom Brunel die?

8. In which year was steam record holder Mallard withdrawn?

9. In which year was the new National Railway Museum at York opened?

10. The Stockton & Darlington Railway opened for business in 1820. True or false?

11. The London & North Western and Lancashire & Yorkshire Railways merged in which year?

12. The 150th anniversary of the Liverpool & Manchester celebrated by a cavalcade at Rainhill in which year?

13. *Royal Scot* visited the United States in which year?

14. Electrification of the Euston-Glasgow West Coast Main Line was completed in which year?

15. In which year was BR's Modernisation Plan published?

Section 4:
Important Dates

PICTURE QUESTION: In which year did the Channel Tunnel open for passenger business?

1. The end of steam on the Southern Region was — when?

2. Britain's first 'Pacific' locomotive was Churchward's *The Great Bear*. In which year was it built?

3. The Lynton & Barnstaple Railway ceased operation in which year?

4. BR's first Standard locomotive No. 70000 *Britannia* was built in which year?

5. In which month and year was the Harrow disaster?

6. When did the first High Speed Train power cars enter traffic?

7. In which month and year did BR finish with steam power?

8. In which year did *City of Truro* reportedly reach 100mph?

9. When did the Somerset & Dorset main line close?

10. In which year was the recent Clapham disaster — 1987, 1988 or 1989?

11. Trains Illustrated was last published as a monthly magazine in December 1961. What replaced it?

12. The 'Great Race to the North' took place in which year?

13. In which year did the Great Western Railway abandon broad gauge?

14. In which year did locomotive engineer Sir Nigel Gresley die?

15. The 'Brighton Belle' last ran in which year?

Section 5:
Facts And Feats

1. Which was BR's first diesel-hydraulic main line locomotive?

2. The Great Eastern Railway built Britain's first 0-10-0 tank locomotive. What was its nickname?

3. What piece of steam locomotive equipment was the Giesl Ejector?

4. What was the wheel arrangement of the largest tank locomotive to run on a British railway?

5. After whom is the diesel engine named?

6. An experimental diesel-mechanical gas-turbine locomotive was built was English Electric in 1961. What was its wheel arrangement and number?

7. In which year did the prototype 'Deltic' take to the rails?

8. The Snowdon Mountain Railway is worked by cables. True or false?

9. The Midland Railway initiated an electric service over a nine-mile route in Lancashire in 1908. Between which two locations?

10. What is Thomas Edmondson (1803-59) credited with inventing?

11. The 'Mallet' articulated locomotive was devised by Anatole Mallet. True or false?

12. Which of the four pre-Nationalisation companies handed over the most steam locomotives to British Railways in 1948, and how many?

13. Which was Britain's first public electric railway in 1883?

14. In feet, how long is the Forth Bridge?

15. The delivery of which shunter represented the end of Class 08 production in 1962?

PICTURE QUESTION: BR's Advanced Passenger Train was developed from 1969 onwards. In which year were experiments abandoned and the units withdrawn from service?

Section 6:
Facts And Feats

1. Which is the highest summit in Britain?

2. Which is the lowest railway point in Britain?

3. In the USA, a steam locomotive was once built to the 2-10-10-2 wheel arrangement. True or false?

4. Which still-used British station has the largest roof span?

5. Britain's first 4-6-0 steam locomotive was the 'Jones Goods' built in 1894. Which railway was it built for?

6. What was the running number of the first British main line diesel-electric locomotive built by the LMS in 1947?

7. To the nearest mile, how long is the Severn Tunnel?

8. China has an estimated 55,000 miles of railway lines. True or false?

9. An ingenious rail clip was invented in 1957 by the Norwegian Per Pende-Rofsen. What is its trade name?

10. The London-Brighton route was the first British main line to be electrified with third rail. In which year was it inaugurated?

11. On which route is the longest straight section of line in the UK, and how long is it?

12. George Bradshaw (1801-53) is associated with which familiar item?

13. What was the nickname of the 4-8-8-4s built between 1941-4 for the Union Pacific Railroad in the USA?

14. Which is the highest station on the British main line network?

15. Which private builder constructed the most DMU cars for British Rail from the 1950s onwards?

PICTURE QUESTION: The 'Deltics' were BR's first production 100mph passenger diesel locomotives - at which depots were they originally allocated?

Section 7:
Famous People

PICTURE QUESTION: Which famous locomotive engineer designed both these locomotives?

1. Who had the famous initials 'IKB'?

2. Class A4 locomotive *Sir Ronald Matthews* was named after whom?

3. Which famous engineer designed *Locomotion*?

4. Of which pre-Grouping company was Lord Faringdon chairman of?

5. William Arrol was responsible for the construction of the Forth Bridge. True or false?

6. Alfred Belpaire is best known for his locomotive firebox design. What nationality was he?

7. Who was the 'Railway King' who died in 1871?

8. Who officially named Class 47 locomotive No. 47541 after herself?

9. Sir Felix Pole was head of which pre-Nationalisation company?

10. Who was the French locomotive engineer who designed 4-8-4 steam locomotive No. 242A1?

11. Valve gear designer Arturo Caprotti (1881-1938) was Italian/Swiss/French?

12. Which engineer is remembered for his double-ended locomotives on the Festiniog Railway?

13. Which 1840 Leicestershire railtour organiser lent his name to a worldwide travel company?

14. Who created a storm in the 1960s with his autobiography 'I Tried to Run a Railway'?

15. Which engineer became general manager of the same North of England railway company?

Section 8:
Famous People

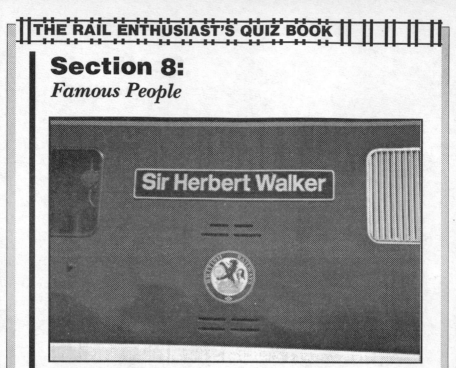

PICTURE QUESTION:Who was Sir Herbert Walker?

To which railway companies did the following Chief Mechanical Engineers belong?

1. A. Sturrock
2. J. C. Park
3. S.D. Holden
4. L.B. Billinton
5. H. Pollitt
6. M. Holmes
7. G. Hughes
8. R.M. Deeley
9. W. Dean
10. F.G. Smith
11. W. Barton Wright

12. F.W. Webb
13. T.E. Haywood
14. T.W. Worsdell
15. W. Marriott
16. H.S. Wainwright
17. R. Urie
18. Sir Daniel Gooch
19. T.W. Worsdell
20. P. Stirling

Section 9:
Nicknames

PICTURE QUESTION: 'Britannia' No. 70013 *Oliver Cromwell* hauled the last BR steam passenger train in 1968 — how much did tickets on the special train cost?

Which railway companies had these nicknames?

1. God's Wonderful Railway
2. Liver & Bacon
3. Long & Narrow
4. Muddle & Goes Nowhere
5. Slow & Dirty
6. Mud, Slush & Lumber
7. Milk & Soda Water
8. Got Nowhere
9. Lord's My Shepherd
10. Gone Completely
11. Linger, Crawl & Delay
12. Money, Sunk & Lost
13. Lose 'em, Mix 'em & Smash 'em
14. Muck, Sludge & Lightning
15. Slow, Mouldy & Jolting

Section 10:
Nicknames

Picture Question: Three famous locomotives were reunited at the National Railway Museum York in 1988 — what was the event?

Which locomotive classes have also been known by the following nicknames?

1. Black Five
2. Tango
3. Mickey Mouse
4. Duffs
5. Streak

6. Slim Jim
7. Mansion House Tank
8. Jersey Lily

9. Pom Pom
10. Syphon

11. Long Tom
12. Teddy Bear
13. Jazzer
14. Crab
15. Chopper

Section 11:
Anagrams

PICTURE QUESTION: France's first TGV (high speed) route opened from Paris to Lyon in which year?

Unscramble these anagrams to find the names of Lcomotive Works, past and present:

1. Winds On
2. Acts On Red
3. Hog Legend
4. I Ever Ruin
5. Rant in Gold

6. Late Owners
7. How rich
8. Ox Stroll
9. I Slow Car
10. Siege Halt

11. Throw Novel Map
12. Be Dry
13. Sew Story
14. Dash Fro
15. Both Grin

16. Gin Clan
17. Trod Rafts
18. Torn Vowel
19. Repay Chill
20. Rot Nog

Section 12:
Stations: True or False?

PICTURE QUESTION: The last Great Northern Railway somersault signals survived on which route?

Which of these following stations really existed?

1. York Minster
2. Peterborough West
3. Norwich Thorpe
4. Scunthorpe & Frodingham
5. Newark Castle

6. Reading West
7. Plymouth Abbey
8. Bristol Bath Road
9. Mountain Ash Oxford Street
10. Cheltenham Racecourse

11. Sittingbourne Midland Road
12. Farnborough North
13. Dorchester South
14. Andover Central
15. Wimbledon Common

16. Wigan North Eastern
17. Lancaster Green Ayre
18. Bedford St James
19. Birmingham Moor Street
20. Horton-in-Ribblesdale Central

Section 13:
True Or False?

PICTURE QUESTION: The new PCV driving vans in the 943xx number series are conversions from Class 302 EMUs. True or false?

True or False?

1. The northern most BR station is Thurso.

2. Class 47 diesel No. 47600 was named *Great Western.*

3. Wansford is a station on the Severn Valley Railway.

4. 'Clacton' electric units belong to Class 308.

5. The LMS 'Coronation' 4-6-2s were also known as 'Big Lizzies'.

6. BR purchased a total of 973 'Austerity' 2-8-0s from the War Department.

7. The Type 3 diesel is in the 1500-2500hp power range.

8. The 2-8-2 wheel arrangement is the 'Mikado'.

9. The prototype BR 'modern' train was code-named XP63.

10. Class 91 electric locomotive 91026 is named *Cock o' The North.*

11. Class A4 4-6-2s were equipped with Kreisbahn blastpipes.

12. Class A3 4-6-2 No. 60100 was named *Spearmint.*

13. The Euston arch was rebuilt in Regents Park.

14. The letters RES stand for Rail Express Services.

15. Class 100 DMUs were built by the Gloucester Rail Carriage & Wagon Co.

Section 14:
True Or False?

PICTURE QUESTION: Former War Department 2-10-0 *Vera Lynn* spent most of its working life in Turkey. True or false?

Are these statements true or false?

1. *Flying Scotsman's* original number was 1472.
2. The Snowdon Mountain Railway is known as a rack line.
3. Ropley is a station on the Mid-Hants Railway.
4. The word 'Deltic' refers to a particular design of diesel locomotive transmission.
5. Class 55 No. D9020 was named *Nimrod*.
6. Blackfriars Bridge crosses the River Avon in Bristol.
7. The French Class 141R was a 2-8-2.
8. The InterCity symbol is a swift.
9. The Redmire freight branch runs westwards from Northallerton.
10. An early British Railways CME was R.A. Ribbles.
11. British Railways built 899 standard steam locomotives.
12. The Class 210 DMU has electric transmission instead of the normal mechanical gear.
13. BR's marketing phrase of the 1980s was: 'We're going there'.
14. Sir Nigel Gresley's final locomotive design was the Class V2.
15. The Pullman coach was devised by Sir George Morrison Pullman.

CHAPTER TWO

Geography
and Engineering

Section 15:
Stations

PICTURE QUESTION:
There are two different designs of platform sign at Altrincham — but why?

Which pre-grouping companies owned these important stations in 1923?

1. Birmingham Snow Hill
2. Bolton Trinity Street
3. Bournemouth Central
4. Bradford Forster Square
5. Charing Cross (London)
6. Edinburgh Waverley
7. Holyhead
8. Hull Paragon
9. Inverness
10. King's Cross (London)
11. Leicester London Road
12. Lincoln Central
13. Liverpool Lime Street
14. Manchester Victoria
15. Margate
16. Marylebone
17. Norwich Thorpe
18. Perth
19. Southampton Central
20. York

Section 16:
Stations

PICTURE QUESTION: Which NSE station was famous for retaining its gas lamps into the 1990s?

In which principal British cities are the following stations?

1. Barrhead
2. Bordesley
3. Cathcart
4. Charlton
5. Crouch Hill

6. Duddeston
7. Easterhouse
8. Forest Gate
9. Gravelly Hill
10. Gunnersbury

11. Humphrey Park
12. Moses Gate
13. Mount Florida
14. Old Hill
15. Patricroft

16. Perry Barr
17. Reddish North
18. South Kenton
19. Springburn
20. Stalybridge

Section 17:
Structures

PICTURE QUESTION: This bridge was built in the early 1980s to serve a completely new UK system? Which system?

1. What is the technical name for the type of design used for the Forth Bridge?

2. Glenfinnan Viaduct on the West Highland Line is notable for its pioneering use of which building material?

3. In which year did the first Tay Bridge collapse?

4. Who designed the original Tay Bridge?

5. Trowse Swing Bridge carries an electrified line into which city?

6. Which Welsh estuary bridge cost £2 million to rebuild during the 1980s?

7. The tallest lattice girder bridge in England was 34 yards long and 196ft high. What was it called?

8. Which bridge crosses the Menai Straight into Anglesey?

9. The 37-span Ouse Valley Viaduct is on which main line?

10. Which so-called Border Bridge does not cross a border?

11. On which preserved line is the 200ft span cast iron Victoria Bridge?

12. Why was the Severn Railway Bridge prematurely demolished?

13. At 1275 yards, the Harringworth Viaduct is reputed to be Britain's longest brick-built structure. Which company built it?

14. A major viaduct is a notable bottleneck at the southern end of the East Coast Main Line. Where is it?

15. Who designed the Saltash Bridge?

Section 18:
Structures

1. Which tunnel has a house built directly over its north portal?

2. How long is the Seikan Tunnel in Japan, the world's longest?

3. When were Parliamentary powers first obtained for the building of the Channel Tunnel?

4. On which route is Crosby Garrett Tunnel?

5. Which is the deepest tunnel in England?

6. In which city is Cowlairs Tunnel?

7. In which year was the decision taken to proceed with construction of the Channel Tunnel?

8. Is Tunnel Junction on the northern or southern outskirts of Worcester?

9. Rolling stock had to be built to a special narrow gauge to traverse which Kentish route?

10. Berwyn Tunnel is on which preserved line?

11. Which is the nearest East Coast Main Line station to Peascliffe Tunnel?

12. In which year did all BR services cease through Woodhead Tunnel?

13. On which closed line was Whitrope Tunnel?

14. A serious fire on the London Underground station in November 1987 cost 31 lives. At which station?

15. A structure on the East Kent Railway is known as Golgotha Tunnel. True or false?

PICTURE QUESTION: Which tunnel on an isolated system has such low clearances that this shunting locomotive had to have its cab height reduced to go through it?

Section 19:
Tunnels

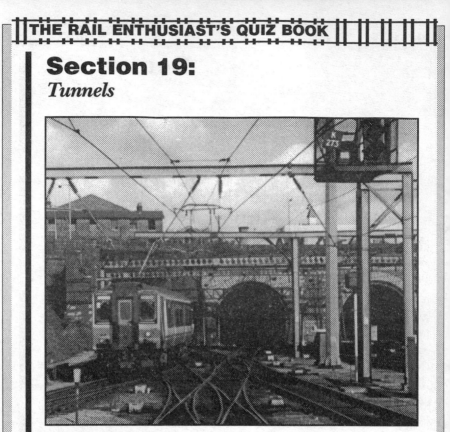

PICTURE QUESTION: One of the busiest tunnels is directly north of London's King's Cross station. Name it.

Name the tunnels between the stations on the following routes:

1. Preston Park-Hassocks
2. Kemble-Stroud
3. Worcester-Droitwich Spa
4. Tiverton Parkway-Taunton
5. Bath-Chippenham

6. Leatherhead-Dorking
7. West Hoathly-Horsted Keynes

8. Newmarket-Kennett
9. Bedford-Wellingborough
10. Edale-Chinley

11. Grantham-Newark
12. Peterborough-Grantham
13. Dore-Grindleford
14. Retford-Gainsborough
15. Marsden-Greenfield

Section 20:
Tunnels

PICTURE QUESTION: Catesby Tunnel was a famous tunnel on a short-lived main line into London, built in 1897 and closed in 1966. Which famous railway company first ran trains through it?

Name the tunnels between the stations on the following routes:

1. Pilning-Caldicot
2. Weeton-Horsforth
3. Ribblehead-Dent
4. Dumfries-Kirkconnel
5. Anniesland-Westerton

6. Castle Cary-Taunton
7. Gillingham-Templecombe
8. Petersfield-Rowlands Castle

9. Dent-Garsdale
10. Settle-Horton-in-Ribblesdale

11. Wellingborough-Bedford
12. Castle Cary-Taunton
13. Churston-Dartmouth
14. Kidderminster-Bewdley
15. Micheldever-Winchester

Section 21:
Stations

PICTURE QUESTION: This once-busy Yorkshire station has been replaced by a new structure alongside. Where is it?

The following towns have two stations, name them:

1. Acton
2. Barry
3. Bedford
4. Bootle
5. Bradford

6. Bristol
7. Bromley
8. Chessington

9. Coatbridge
10. Dorchester

11. Dumbarton
12. Enfield
13. Ewell
14. Falkirk
15. Gainsborough

Section 22:
Summits

PICTURE QUESTION: In steam days, trains on Copy Pit Summit often needed a banker — which depot supplied the last Class 8F 2-8-0s for this duty in 1968?

Name the famous summits between these stations on the following routes:

1. Newton Abbot-Totnes
2. Taunton-Tiverton
3. Forsinard-Altnabreac
4. Dingwall-Garve
5. Inverness-Carrbridge

6. Garelochhead-Arrochar
7. Dalwhinnie-Blair Atholl
8. Carstairs-Kingsknowe

9. Lockerbie-Auchinleck
10. Girvan-Barrhill

11. Garsdale-Kirkby Stephen
12. Oxenholme-Penrith
13. Hebden Bridge-Burnley
14. Marsden-Greenfield
15. Caersws-Machynlleth

Section 23:
On The Line

PICTURE QUESTION: The Brush Locomotive Works stands alongside which main line station?

1. How many miles is it from King's Cross to Edinburgh Waverley?

2. Which route is known as the 'Swan Line'?

3. Where is Basford Hall Yard?

4. The now-closed Fen Drayton sand quarry was on which branch?

5. A large GWR signal box survives at Sutton Bridge Junction — where is this?

6. Millerhill Yard is at the north end of which now-closed main line?

7. Off which line is the branch to Sizewell power station?

8. Georgemas Junction is at the midway point of which northern Scottish towns?

9. The spur to Brentford waste terminal joins the West of England main line at which location?

10. Clifton Down Tunnel is in which city?

11. Which new public transport system now uses the refurbished Nunnery Sidings?

12. Where is Long Rock depot?

13. Fishguard Harbour is the ferry point for which Irish port?

14. Three Spires Junction is on the northern outskirts of which city?

15. Ferrybridge Power Station is closest to which BR locomotive depot?

Section 24:
On The Line

1. Where are Laverstock North and South Junctions?

2. Wemyss Bay is the terminus for electric services from which principal Glasgow terminus?

3. Where was Whitemoor marshalling yard?

4. How high is Corrour Summit on the West Highland Line?

5. What was the major freight traffic most recently generated at Chard Junction?

6. The Taunton Cider Company's sidings are at the main line junction to which preserved line?

7. Where is Ripple Lane Yard?

8. Which former Great Western terminus station never had any track?

9. Lelant and Lelant Sidings are both stations on which Cornish branch?

10. In which city is Lawley Street container terminal?

11. Next to which network station will the Bluebell Railway's eventual northern terminus be?

12. Where does a main line passenger change to join the Henley-on-Thames branch?

13. Which route is known as the 'Robin Hood Line'?

14. Where is Belmont Yard?

15. Kirkham & Wesham is the junction of two lines to the same town. Which one?

PICTURE QUESTION: Which London depot is responsible for the maintenance of High Speed Trains for West of England services?

CHAPTER THREE

Terminology

Section 25:
Steam Terminology

PICTURE QUESTION: What is the name of the valve gear carried by No. 71000 *Duke of Gloucester*?

1. What is the 'Consolidation' wheel arrangement?

2. Inside what is the brick arch positioned?

3. What is a 'buckeye'?

4. Where is the water kept on a well tank locomotive?

5. What is the terminology for locomotives used for both passenger and freight trains?

6. What is the interior of the cab known as?

7. The name Lemaitre is associated with which item?

8. Which BR locomotives were known as 'Space Ships'?

9. What is the function of the injector?

10. What is the Whyte system?

11. What is the name of the driver's main control handle?

12. Where would you find stays?

13. What nationality was Herbert Garratt?

14. Many Midland Railway 4-4-0s used steam twice. What was this called?

15. What trackside structures allowed steam locomotives to replenish their water supply at speed?

Section 26:
Steam Terminology

PICTURE QUESTION: Was the firebox of a Bulleid Pacific — this one belongs to No. 35025 – made from copper or steel?

1. What is a 'Spam Can'?
2. What is a capuchon?
3. What were 'Kreigsloks'?
4. What were wing plates?
5. What was the 'cod's mouth' on an LNER Class A4 Pacific?
6. What is a 'blow back'?
7. What was ACFI apparatus?
8. What is 'clag'?
9. What is the purpose of the injector?
10. What is a 'hot box'?
11. What happened to many main line LMS locomotives when they were 'de-frocked'?
12. Which wheel arrangement, never used in Britain, was nicknamed the 'Centipede'?
13. Why did lineside staff fear 'Sky Rockets'?
14. What was a 'Flying Bedstead'?
15. What external fitments were often known as 'Blinkers'?

Section 27
Steam Terminology

With which principal part of the steam locomotive is the following terminology associated — boiler, cab, or wheels?

1. Crosshead
2. Dome
3. Snifting valve
4. Connecting rod
5. Regulator handle

6. Top feed
7. Roof stays
8. Reversing gear

9. Water gauge
10. Fusible plug

11. Rocking grate levers
12. Balancing weight
13. Tube plate
14. Damper control
15. Horn guides

PICTURE QUESTION: GWR-inspired gas-turbine locomotive No. 18000 spent 30 years in which country?

Section 28:
Modern Terminology

1. Is a pantograph used on a diesel or electric locomotive?
2. What does a collector shoe do?
3. What type of transmission did the experimental 'Fell' diesel locomotive have?
4. How man axles does a 1Co-Co1 locomotive have?
5. What is the standard overhead voltage for British electrified lines?
6. What is the DSD?
7. What is the horsepower rating of the General Motors Class 59?
8. What is the principal function of a circuit-breaker?
9. What is a 'Skinhead'?
10. What equipment replaced the main generator in refurbished Class 37 diesel locomotives?
11. What equipment did Stones, Spanner and Clayton build for diesel locomotives?
12. What are often 'nose-suspended'?
13. Electro-diesel locomotives collect electric power from the third rail to power the diesel engine. True or false?
14. Is a rectifier found on a diesel or electric locomotive?
15. What are described as of the 'Commonwealth' design?

PICTURE QUESTION: What major electrical operation takes place while Thameslink trains call at London's Farringdon station?

Section 29:
Modern Terminology

PICTURE QUESTION: The Class 59 General Motors locomotives were built in America — but where?

1. Which type of BR locomotives used Wilson-Drewry gearboxes?

2. Which British non-railway firm built many Sulzer engines under licence in the 1960s and also refurbished the Class 47?

3. Which BR locomotives often ran with match trucks to ensure operation of track circuit equipment?

4. The technical specification caused which sub-class of BR diesel to be nicknamed 'Pushers' and 'Bagpipes'?

5. What is currently the most common coupling symbol seen on BR diesel locomotives?

6. Which current British electric locomotive class has the fastest speed capability?

7. In which piece of equipment is the 'A frame' in a diesel locomotive?

8. What is 'collecting the juice'?

9. What is the three-letter code for the conventional Sulzer engine — LDA, DLA or RDA?

10. The Voith company built which equipment for diesel-hydraulic locomotives?

11. What type of power unit is carried by most High Speed Train power cars?

12. What wheel arrangement is the BR Class 31 diesel?

13. Bogie flash guards are fitted to which specific sub-class of locomotives?

14. When the early BR diesel locomotives were built with headcode discs — how many were fitted to each end?

15. Which liquid is the most common form of engine coolant on BR?

Section 30:
Modern Technology

PICTURE QUESTION: What type of braking system did the Southern Railway incorporate in its principal commuter units of the 1940s?

With which principal part of the diesel and electric locomotive is the following terminology associated — power equipment, cab, or body?

1. Headcode box
2. Horn valve
3. Compressor
4. AWS indicator
5. ETH jumper socket

6. Sand box
7. Wiper motor
8. Fluid coupling

9. Tap changer
10. Reservoir pipe

11. Power controller
12. Traction motor
13. Marker lights
14. Sanding button
15. Turbocharger

Section 31:
Abbreviations

PICTURE QUESTION:
This gate adorns a
London terminus station.
Where is the gate, and
what do the letters
represent?

Which railway companies were well-known by the following abbreviations?

1. CK&PR
2. CLC
3. CV&HR
4. F&MJR
5. GN&GE

6. GNSR
7. G&SWR
8. LB&SCR
9. LNWR
10. LT&SR

11. M&GNJC
12. MS&LR
13. M&SWJR
14. N&BR
15. NBR

16. NSR
17. PD&SWJR
18. SECR
19. TVR
20. WC&PR

Section 32:
Abbreviations

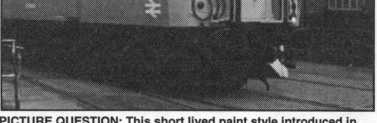

PICTURE QUESTION: This short lived paint style introduced in 1985 was popularly known as 'Jaffa Cake', but officially belonged to the L&SE operation — what was this short for?

These abbreviations are all in common railway use today. What do they stand for?

1. APT
2. APTIS
3. CEM
4. CWR
5. EPB

6. ETH
7. FRED
8. HST
9. MGR
10. OHL

11. PACT
12. PSO
13. RETB
14. SSI
15. TDM

16. TESCO
17. TOPS
18. TOU
19. TSR
20. UTS

Section 33:
Multiple Unit Codes

Identify the following rolling stock codes:

1. DMBS
2. TCL
3. TFK
4. DTBS
5. DMBC

6. TBFKL
7. TS
8. TC
9. TSLRB
10. DTBS

11. BDTCOL
12. TSOL
13. MBSO
14. MPMV
15. DMSO

16. DTSO
17. DMPV
18. MSO
19. TFOLH
20. BDM

PICTURE QUESTION: This multiple unit has been refurbished for service into the late 1990s. Who built it?

Section 34:
Coaching Stock Codes

PICTURE QUESTION: The East Coast Main Line is now served by these fixed formations — of how many vehicles, including the locomotive?

What do these coaching stock codes mean?

1. BFO
2. BG
3. BPOT
4. BSK
5. CK

6. DBSO
7. DLV
8. FO
9. GUV
10. LFK

11. POS
12. RBR
13. RFM
14. RK
15. RMBT

16. SK
17. SLEP
18. TGS
19. TS
20. TSOD

CHAPTER FOUR

Steam Locomotives

Section 35:
GWR 'Castle' Class

1. What was the final total of 'Castles', new build and conversion?

2. Over what time span was the construction programme?

3. What was the name and number of the last 'Castle'?

4. Who was credited the 'Castle' design?

5. No. 7000 was named after the last chairman of the GWR — who?

6. The GWR's only 4-6-2 was rebuilt into which 'Castle' in 1924?

7. How many 'Stars' were rebuilt as 'Castles'?

8. Which 'Castle' is preserved at the Science Museum in London?

9. No. 4082 *Windsor Castle* swapped identity with which other class member in 1952?

10. What is the longest name ever carried by a 'Castle'?

11. Which 'Castle' featured in exchange trials with the LNER?

12. *100A1 Lloyds* was the first 'Castle' withdrawal three months before the delivery of the last-built example. In which month and year was it taken out of service?

13. To which country was No. 4079 *Pendennis Castle* exported in 1977?

14. How many cylinders has a 'Castle'?

15. Which preservation centre was the first home of No. 7029 *Clun Castle*?

PICTURE QUESTION: Castle' Class No. 7029 *Clun Castle* hauled the last booked BR passenger out of a London terminus. Which station, and in what year?

Section 36:
GWR 'King' Class

PICTURE QUESTION: Which company sponsored the return to steam of No. 6000 *King George V*?

1. When was first 'King' No. 6000 introduced?

2. How many were built?

3. Who presented the bell carried by No. 6000?

4. How many cylinders does the 'King' have — three or four?

5. Who was the designer of the 'King' Class?

6. In which year were the 'Kings' withdrawn from BR service?

7. Which 'King' was partially streamlined for a period in 1935?

8. What are the numbers of the two 'Kings' were rescued from Barry scrapyard?

9. Where is No. 6023 being restored?

10. What was the cabside weight symbol carried the 'King' Class?

11. The 'King' weighs 135 tons in working order? True or false?

12. Which two Kings were renamed after then current monarchs, and who were they?

13. Which 'King' was resurrected from the scrapline for a final railtour?

14. What was the 'King's' power classification on BR?

15. No. 6024 spent the early years of its preservation at which site from 1973?

Section 37:
GWR Passenger Classes

PICTURE QUESTION: What is the BR power classification of No. 6998 *Burton Agnes Hall*?

1. Parts from which withdrawn class were re-used in the Manors?

2. How many 'County' Class locomotives were built?

3. Who designed the 'Grange' Class 4-6-0?

4. Which was the 'Hall' rebuilt from a 'Saint'?

5. Where is Burton Agnes Hall preserved?

6. Over what time span were 'Manors' built at Swindon?

7. Who was credited with the design of the 'Modified Hall' Class?

8. Which 'Hall' was destroyed in an air raid in 1941?

9. The last 'Grange' was withdrawn in which year?

10. What was the name of the first 'County' No. 1000?

11. What was the BR power classification of the 'County' Class?

12. The last regular passenger duties for the 'Manors' were over which pre-Grouping company's route?

13. How many 'Granges' are preserved?

14. Which preserved 'Hall' is to be rebuilt into a 'Saint'?

15. Which is the only preserved 'Manor' not to have been rescued from Barry scrapyard?

Section 38:
GWR Tender Classes

**PICTURE QUESTION: No. 7828 *Odney Manor* has been preserved
— how many other 'Manors' still exist?**

1. In 1903, 4-4-2 No. 102 was imported from the Continent for comparison trials. What was its name?

2. Which broad gauge 2-2-2 was scrapped in 1906, to be constructed as a replica in 1925?

3. How many 4700 Class 2-8-0s were built — 9, 18 or 27?

4. What wheel arrangement was the 'Aberdare' Class built between 1899-1902?

5. How many 2800 Class 2-8-0s were built, and between which dates?

6. The Earl names of the 9000 Class 4-4-0s were transferred to which class?

7. The National Railway Museum is home to which GWR 2-8-0?

8. Record-breaker *City of Truro* has carried which two numbers during its existence?

9. Which 0-6-0 class was sent to France during the First World War?

10. The 'Duke of Cornwall' and 'Bulldog' classes were rebuilt into which class?

11. Churchward's large class mixed-traffic 2-6-0 introduced in 1911 belonged to which class?

12. How many Robinson 2-8-0s were bought by the GWR from the Government?

13. Which 'Star' is preserved in the National Collection?

14. Class 2800 Class 2-0s converted to oil burners were numbered into which series?

15. A 'Saint' 4-6-0 is being reconstructed by the Great Western Society at Didcot. What will its number be?

Section 39:
GWR Tank Classes

1. What was the nickname of the 2-6-2Ts?

2. What was final GWR design of steam locomotive?

3. Which London system employed Pannier Tanks until 1970?

4. Preserved 9400 Class No. 9466 was built at — Crewe, Swindon or Newcastle?

5. In which year did Hawksworth introduce his 1500 Class 0-6-0PT?

6. Which GWR engine starred in the film 'Titfield Thunderbolt'?

7. What was the number series of the 2-8-2Ts converted from 2-8-0Ts from the 1934 onwards?

8. What was the BR power classification of the 2-8-2T?

9. The GWR purchased six 1101 Class 0-4-0Ts from which private builder in 1926?

10. For which area were the Collett 56xx tanks designed?

11. Which 2-6-2T visited Swindon Works for a complete overhaul in 1971?

12. Three push-pull 0-6-0PTs have been preserved from one class — which?

13. Where was the northernmost depot employing GW-design locomotives?

14. Which modern 0-6-0PT, now preserved, worked with two sisters at a Coventry Colliery until 1969?

15. How many 5700 Class Pannier Tanks were built — 386, 683, or 863?

PICTURE QUESTION: What was the original number series of the Class 14xx 0-4-2Ts when first built?

Section 40:
GWR Pre-Grouping Classes

1. Preserved Taff Vale Class 01 No. 28 was sold by the GWR in 1927. Who was the designer?

2. What was the name of BR No. 1?

3. Which Cambrian Railways tender locomotive class survived into 1954?

PICTURE QUESTION: The Vale of Rheidol Railway's No. 9 is the only surviving original locomotive. Who built it and when?

4. Which small Kerr Stuart 0-4-0ST is preserved with the same number 4 it has carried though four ownerships?

5. Cardiff Railways 0-4-0ST No. 1338 was built in 1898 by which private firm?

6. Which former Sandy & Potton Railway engine did the GWR buy in 1946 for preservation?

7. GWR No. 813 was saved from industrial service. Who originally owned it?

8. How many Vale of Rheidol-design 2-6-2Ts survive?

9. Which home-grown South Wales locomotive wheel type was supplanted by the standard GWR 56xx Class?

10. *The Earl* and *The Countess* belonged to which narrow gauge line?

11. *Kidwelly* and *Cwm Mawr* were once in the ownership of which company?

12. Two former LB&SCR 'Terriers' fell into the hands of the GWR via which line?

13. An 1878 North Pembroke & Fishguard Railway locomotive is exhibited at Scolton Manor Museum. What is its name?

14. The Talyllyn's *Sir Haydn* originally came from which minor railway?

15. Which is the only survivor of the former Alexandra Docks Railway fleet, and where is exhibited?

Section 41:
SR 'Merchant Navy' Class

PICTURE QUESTION: No. 35012 is way off territory on this special working — where is it?

1. What was the original number of the first-built?

2. What was its name?

3. How many were built after Nationalisation?

4. What was the driving wheel diameter?

5. Which works built the 'Merchant Navies'?

6. What word was carried on the circular smokebox plate?

7. What is the name of the non-spoked wheels carried by the class?

8. Who was responsible for the reconstruction programme?

9. Which was the first to be rebuilt and when?

10. What type of valve gear did the rebuilt examples carry?

11. In what year did withdrawals begin?

12. How many are now preserved?

13. Which was the first MN rescued from Barry scrapyard?

14. Where did *Clan Line* spend its earliest time of preservation?

15. Which example is sectioned at the National Railway Museum?

Section 42:
SR 'West Country' and 'Battle of Britain'

PICTURE QUESTION: Enthusiasts admire No. 34037 at Waterloo on June 1967 — is the locomotive a 'Battle of Britain' or 'West Country'?

1. How many locomotives were built?

2. When was the first example built?

3. What was the wheel arrangement?

4. Which works other than Eastleigh built examples?

5. What was the BR number series of the 'West Countries'?

6. What was their final BR power classification?

7. What was the name of the locomotive fitted with a Giesl Ejector?

8. Which three locomotives took part in the 1948 Locomotive Exchanges?

9. What was the original number of the first 'Battle of Britain' locomotive?

10. How many of the class were rebuilt without streamlined casing?

11. Which locomotive was the last to undergo rebuilding in 1961?

12. In which month and year were the final withdrawals made?

13. Which locomotive was sold for preservation in full working order?

14. No. 34051 *Winston Churchill* hauled the statesman's funeral train. In which year?

15. Which Keighley-based 'West Country' was the first to return to the main line?

Section 43:
SR 'Lord Nelson', 'Schools' and 'King Arthurs'

1. Where and when were the 'Lord' Nelsons built?

2. How many 'Lord Nelsons' were built?

3. How many cylinders has the 'Lord Nelson'?

4. Which 'Lord Nelson' was experimentally built with smaller wheels?

5. Where was first-built No. 850 *Lord Nelson* located during the 1980s and 1990s?

6. What was the Southern Railway's class letter for the 'Schools' class?

7. When was the 'Schools' Class introduced?

8. 'Schools' Class No. 30923 carried two names during its career. What were they?

9. Which 'Schools' locomotive was preserved for many years in North America before return to the UK?

10. For what purpose were eight 'Schools' tenders saved from scrapping?

11. Which two designers are credited with the 'King Arthur' Class?

12. In which year did the first 'King Arthur' emerge?

13. What was the total number of 'King Arthur' locomotives built, and what were their original numbers?

14. In which year were the last 'King Arthurs' withdrawn from BR service?

15. Which 'King Arthur' was named after the famous monarch himself?

PICTURE QUESTION: No. 777 *Sir Lamiel* visited a London station in 1986 — do you recognise it?

- 54 -

Section 44:
SR Tank and 'Leader' Classes

PICTURE QUESTION: The Class W 2-6-4T is the tank equivalent of which Maunsell tender design?

1. Where did the USA Class 0-6-0Ts spend most of their working life?

2. Which 2-6-4T was involved in the disastrous 1927 derailment?

3. What wheel arrangement was the Maunsell Class Z?

4. How many Class Zs were built?

5. What was BR number series for Class Z?

6. When was the first Class W tank built?

7. The Class W tank engine survived in BR service until which year?

8. How many cylinders did the Class W have?

9. The final duties for the Class Ws were banking between which two Exeter stations?

10. Six tank locomotives were built by Armstrong Whitworth from spare Maunsell parts for which railway?

11. Who designed the ill-fated 'Leader' Class?

12. How many 'Leaders' were actually completed?

13. What was the 'Leader's' number series?

14. SR No. 949 *Hecate* was purchased in 1932 by the SR from which private line?

15. *River Frome* was the only example of which ill-fated class?

Section 45:
SR Tank Classes

PICTURE QUESTION: This Wainwright Class C 0-6-0 was retained as Ashford Works shunter No. DS239. Where is it now preserved?

1. What was the Class designation of Bulleid's 'Austerity' 0-6-0s of 1942?

2. What was their unusual number series in Southern Railway days?

3. In its original form, what was the wheel-arrangement of the Class U1 locomotive?

4. Maunsell's last design was 20 Class Q - what as their number series?

5. What was the BR power classification of the Qs?

6. Which LB&SCR 4-4-2 was used for trials for Bulleid's ill-fated 'Leader' Class?

7. Which were the last British design of inside-cylinder 4-4-0s?

8. How many Class N1 locomotives were built?

9. The Class N1 has three cylinders - true or false?

10. Fifty Class Ns were built from 1925 from parts manufactured at which Government-owned factory?

11. How many Class Us were converted from 'River Tanks'.

12. No. 31806 is the only surviving 'River' conversion - what was its former name?

13. Two Urie 4-6-0s have been preserved - what are their numbers?

14. Which Class S15 was sold in two halves - wheels and boiler - to two separate preservation groups?

15. Which locomotive was named Greene King after preservation?

Section 46:
SR Pre-Grouping Classes

PICTURE QUESTION: Two locomotives on the Isle of Wight — which pre-Grouping companies built them?

1. Which branch was the final haunt of the Beattie 0298 Class 2-4-0WTs?

2. What name is attached to the Billinton LB&SC Class E4 0-6-2T at the Bluebell Railway?

3. What was the class designation of Adams LSWR 0-4-4Ts sent to the Isle of Wight?

4. 0-4-2 No. 216 *Gladstone* was preserved as long ago as 1927. True or false?

5. What was the nickname of the ungainly Drummond Class T14 4-6-0s as first built?

6. What class and number is Bluebell on the Bluebell Railway?

7. What was the wheel arrangement of the massive Billinton 'Baltic' tanks as built?

8. The first of Stroudley's 'Terriers' was built in which year?

9. The German firm of Borsig delivered some Class L1 4-4-0s just before the outbreak of war. Where was the factory?

10. When was the first Drummond 4-6-0 No. 330 introduced to the London & South Western Railway?

11. The Lyme Regis branch was the last haunt of which Adams 4-4-2T?

12. What was the name of Brighton's war memorial engine?

13. How many LSWR Class M7 0-4-4Ts are preserved?

14. The East Somerset Railway is home to the only-surviving Class E1 locomotive No. 110. What was its original name on the LB&SCR?

15. Which class was replaced at Southampton Docks by the USA Class 0-6-0T?

Section 47:
LMS 'Princess Royal' & 'Duchess' Classes

PICTURE QUESTION: 'Duchess' No. 46229 stands outside the works where it was overhauled in 1976. Which works?

1. What was the original number of the first 'Princess Royal' Pacific?

2. Where was it built and when?

3. When was the last member of the class withdrawn from BR service?

4. Which 'Princess Royal' had unique outside valve motion?

5. What was the name and number of the 1952 'Turbomotive' conversion?

6. What was its fate?

7. Where the two preserved examples now based?

8. What the real identity of 'Duchess' No. 6220 which went to the USA in 1939?

9. Which 'Duchess' was named after its designer — and what was his name?

10. Which 'Duchess' was never LMS-owned?

11. To which region was mass transfer considered in the early 1960s?

12. What the last year of BR operation?

13. Which holiday camp owner bought Nos. 46229 and 46233 in 1963/4?

14. No. 46244 *King George VI* was renamed in 1941 — from what?

15. Was the preserved No. 46235 *City of Birmingham* ever streamlined?

Section 48:
LMS Passenger Classes

PICTURE QUESTION: A scruffy 'Jubilee' in its final days - what was No. 45627 named?

1. When did the first 'Royal Scot' locomotive enter traffic as new?

2. How many 'Royal Scots' were eventually in service?

3. Which private contractor built the entire 'Royal Scot' class?

4. How many cylinders has a 'Royal Scot', three or four?

5. What was the LMS number and name of the 'Royal Scot' which was converted from high-pressure locomotive *Fury*?

6. What was the final BR power classification for the 'Royal Scot'?

7. Identify the only 'Royal Scot' fitted with BR-type smoke deflectors.

8. What is the true identity of preserved No. 46100?

9. How many 'Jubilees' were rebuilt with larger boilers from 1942 onwards?

10. Which 'Jubilee' was destroyed in the 1952 Harrow disaster?

11. What was the original name of No. 45700 *Amethyst*?

12. From which depot were the last 'Jubilees' withdrawn in 1967?

13. What is the main physical difference between preserved No. 45596 and its present-day counterparts?

14. Which ex-Barry 'Jubilee' is restored to working order?

15. Where is it now normally kept?

Section 49:
LMS Standard Classes

PICTURE QUESTION: One of these 'Black Fives' was built after Nationalisation by BR — which one?

1. Which famous 'Black Five' was used in the film 'The Virgin Soldiers' and then scrapped?

2. Which two other members of the class hauled BR's last steam passenger train in 1968?

3. Identify the Class 5 preserved at the National Railway Museum, and its builder.

4. Over what timespan were the 'Black Fives' built?

5. How many 'Black Fives' were built?

6. What type of motion is carried by the unique preserved No. 44767?

7. What was the lowest numbered Class 5?

8. How many Class 5s originally carried names?

9. Which named 'Black Five' lasted until the end of BR steam?

10. What were the final three BR depots to house 'Black Fives' to the end of BR steam?

11. The original Class 8F emerged from Crewe Works in which year?

12. Which LNER works also built 68 LMS-design 2-8-0s?

13. When built, some 8Fs became LNER Class O6. True or false?

14. Ex-WD (now preserved) No. 48773 did not enter service on BR until which year?

15. How many of the 852 8Fs built saw service on BR?

Section 50:
LMS Tender Classes

1. Which independent company employed five Fowler-design 0-6-0 Class 4F tender engines?

2. Which preserved line is home for the sole-preserved Ivatt Class 4MT 2-6-0?

3. An LNWR-design 4-6-0 was built in 1925 for the British Empire Exhibition — which class?

4. The LMS built 175 Class 7F locomotives which were outlived by the LNWR design they superseded. What was their wheel arrangement and final BR number series?

5. Which was the first entirely new LMS tender design, influenced by Horwich practice?

6. Beyer-Garratts were built to haul what type of traffic on the Midland Main Line?

7. What was the wheel arrangement of the LMS Beyer-Garratt?

8. How many Stanier Class 5 2-6-0s were built?

9. From which class of locomotive were the first 'Patriot' 4-6-0s nominally rebuilt?

10. How many 'Patriots' were eventually built?

11. BR purchased three locomotives from the Government in 1957. What type were they?

12. In which year did Sir Henry Fowler assume control of locomotive design?

13. Five LMS Hughes 2-6-0s were fitted with modified valve gear in 1953? What type?

14. The first Ivatt Class 4MT 2-6-0s were introduced in 1947 with double chimneys. True or false?

15. What is the LMS number of the Class 4F 0-6-0 preserved at the Midland Railway Centre?

PICTURE QUESTION: What was the nickname given to this ugly LMS-design 2-6-0 in its later years?

Section 51:
LMS Tank Classes

PICTURE QUESTION: Ivatt designed the LMS 2-6-2T — but was it H.A. Ivatt or H.G. Ivatt?

1. What wheel arrangement was the 1930 tank engine LMS No. 1?

2. What was its number under BR ownership?

3. Which route employed the Stanier 3-cylinder 2-6-4Ts?

4. What was the number of the final LMS-designed locomotive delivered in 1954?

5. What is the nickname of the LMS Class 3F 0-6-0T?

6. After Nationalisation, some LMS-design 2-6-4Ts were built at the former Southern Railway works at Eastleigh. True or false?

7. Which LMS designer who assumed office is only credited with one tank design?

8. What was the short-lived name applied to No. 2313?

9. To which country were two regauged Class 3F 0-6-0Ts, Nos. 7456 and 7553, despatched in August 1944?

10. Ten 4-6-4Ts to a pre-Grouping company design were turned out in 1924. Which company?

11. Which two LMS-design 2-6-4Ts are preserved on the Lakeside & Haverthwaite Railway?

12. What was Sir William Stanier's first locomotive design in 1932?

13. What was the power classification of the Ivatt 2-6-2T?

14. How many Ivatt 2-6-2Ts were built before production was switched to a BR version?

15. Twenty-nine more heavy duty LNWR tanks were constructed by the LMS in 1923, but all were withdrawn by 1950 — what was their wheel arrangement?

Section 52:
LMS Pre-Grouping Classes

1. What was the final working place of the Midland Class 1F 0-6-0Ts?

2. How many Class 7F 2-8-0s were built by the Midland for the Somerset & Dorset Line?

PICTURE QUESTION: Which pre-grouping company used this 0-6-0T No. 58850?

3. What was the nickname of the Caledonian Railway's Drummond 0-4-0STs introduced in 1885?

4. What was the surname of the two LT&S Chief Engineers who designed the company's tank locomotive classes after 1900?

5. In 1925, the LMS purchased and set to work 20 2-8-0s of another company's design. Whose?

6. What was the wheel arrangement of the Midland Railway's 1919 banking engine nicknamed 'Big Bertha'?

7. On which incline was 'Big Bertha' employed?

8. Which Midland Compound is preserved at York?

9. The Bluebell Railway is now home for Class 2F 0-6-0T No. 58850. Which company built it?

10. Which Scottish pre-Grouping company's locomotive fleet was reduced to just one at Nationalisation?

11. Which Highland 'Small Ben' Class 4-4-0 was saved for preservation after withdrawal, and later scrapped?

12. The Caledonian Railway's 4-2-2 No. 123 is preserved — where?

13. Which company's final design of 0-6-2Ts survived into the 1960s in industrial service at Walkden Colliery, Manchester?

14. Which Highland Railway tender design of 1915 were considered too heavy and immediately sold to the Caledonian Railway?

15. What wheel arrangement was the Caledonian 'Dunalastair' design?

Section 53:
LNER A4 Class

PICTURE QUESTION: No. 60007 *Sir Nigel Gresley* was built in which year?

1. When was the first Class A4 built?

2. Which Class A4 holds the world speed record for steam at 126mph?

3. What was its BR number?

4. Where was the record achieved and when?

5. How many A4s were built?

6. What was the number of the A4 destroyed by a bomb at York in April 1942?

7. Which name has been carried by two different A4s?

8. Which A4 had its name transferred from a Class A1?

9. Preserved No. 60007 was the 150th Pacific designed by Sir Nigel Gresley. True or false?

10. What was the original livery of the first four A4s built?

11. What has preserved 60019 *Bittern* been masquerading in recent years?

12. Which depot had the London allocation until 1963?

13. From which region were the final examples withdrawn in 1966?

14. Which A4 was the last to be overhauled at Doncaster Works?

15. Which A4s are preserved in North America?

Section 54:
LNER A1-A3 Classes

PICTURE QUESTION: This famous Class A2 4-6-2 was loaned to a preserved line at the end of 1992. Can you recognise the depot location?

1. What was the original LNER class designation of the Gresley 4-6-2?

2. Which locomotive was exhibited at the 1925 British Empire Exhibition?

3. Which company built the first Gresley Pacific in 1922?

4. What final front end modification was carried out to A3s in the early 1960s?

5. What was the name of the last survivor of Class A3 on BR in 1966?

6. How many Class A2s were built or converted?

7. Which designer was honoured by the Class A2 No. 500?

8. Class A2/2 was a rebuild of which wheel arrangement?

9. Which Scottish depot took three Class A2s in 1963 to replace LMS Pacifics?

10. Which Class A2 is preserved?

11. Which was the Gresley Pacific rebuilt into the prototype Class A1/1 in 1945?

12. Which works built the production Class A1s, and how many?

13. How many A1s were equipped with roller bearing axleboxes?

14. Which A1 locomotive was named after a trade union official?

15. What is the number and name allocated to the new Class A1 4-6-2 currently under construction?

Section 55:
LNER Passenger Classes

PICTURE QUESTION: The North Norfolk Railway's Class B12 is now unique in Britain in which principal respect?

1. Who designed Class V2?

2. What was V2 *Green Arrow* named after?

3. What was the V2 number series in BR ownership?

4. The V2s had three cylinders. True or false?

5. What was their BR power classification?

6. What animals were the first 40 Class B1s named after?

7. Which Class B1 was destroyed in an accident in 1950?

8. Which preserved B1 has the same name as the scrapped No. 61379?

9. What was the final role of many B1s after withdrawal from active use?

10. Which B1 was the only LNER-design locomotive to reach Barry scrapyard?

11. To which remote area were many of the Great Eastern Class B12s despatched in the 1930s?

12. What sporting links did many of the B17s have?

13. Name the two streamlined Class B17s?

14. What class designation was given Class B17s to those rebuilt by Edward Thompson?

15. What classification of boiler did the Thompson rebuilds carry?

Section 56:
LNER Tender Classes

PICTURE QUESTION: LNER No 143 — to which Class did it belong?

1. LNER No. 1863 belonged to a unique class. What was it?

2. The preserved *The Great Marquess* was designed for which route?

3. *Bantam Cock* was the first built of how many Class V4s?

4. Who designed the 'Claud Hamilton' 4-4-0?

5. The Butler Henderson Class was a design of which railway?

6. Which Government agency ordered hundreds of Robinson 2-8-0s for its own use?

7. The two preserved North Eastern 0-8-0s come from which LNER classes?

8. Which design was nicknamed the 'Pom-Pom'?

9. Several Class J36s were named after their involvement in which event?

10. What was the LNER Class letter for the 4-4-2 wheel arrangement?

11. The Worsdell Class J27 survived in BR service to the end of 1967 - in which area of Britain?

12. Was is the name of the preserved Class D34 'Glen' 4-4-0?

13. How many Thompson Class K1 2-6-0s were built between 1949-50?

14. *Yorkshire* was the name of the first-built example of which class?

15. What the original number of Gresley's 'Hush-Hush' 4-6-4?

Section 57:
LNER Tank Classes

PICTURE QUESTION: Which railway company built this Class N7 0-6-2T, and what is its correct BR number?

1. The LNER bought 75 'Austerity' 0-6-0STs from the Ministry of Supply — what was their Class number?

2. What was the wheel arrangement of Thompson's 1945 Class L1?

3. How many L1s were built?

4. Which 1898 design was perpetuated with a new batch of 28 locomotives built by BR?

5. What was the BR number series of Gresley's Class V1/V3 Class?

6. Which route was the haunt of the last BR survivors of the 'Austerity' 0-6-0ST design?

7. Which tank engine design worked until 1965 as Doncaster Works shunters?

8. Which company supplied the LNER with vertical-boilered locomotives?

9. Which class was created in 1931 by Gresley's rebuild of the Raven 4-4-4T?

10. The Class N5 0-6-2T was built at Darlington. True or false?

11. The final series of Class N2s were built by the LNER with condensing gear for working to which London destination?

12. How many cylinders did the Class V1s have?

13. In what year were the last Class V3 survivors withdrawn?

14. What is the name of the preserved 0-6-0T No. 69023?

15. Where is the much-travelled preserved Class N2 0-6-2T based?

Section 58:
LNER Pre-Grouping Classes

1. Which Great Eastern tank was nicknamed the 'Coffee Pot'?

2. Which company employed the Class Y9 0-4-0 dock tank?

3. What was the class letter for the 0-8-4T wheel arrangement?

4. William Worsdell designed a 4-8-0T for heavy shunting. What was its BR designation?

PICTURE QUESTION: GNR-design Class J52 No. 1247 was built by which company?

5. Which North British class suffered its first casualty when No. 68341 slipped into Kirkcaldy Harbour?

6. To which country and place did preserved Class J52 No. 1247 visit in 1991?

7. Which Class J69 tank was repainted in Great Eastern blue as Liverpool Street pilot in the early 1960s?

8. What wheel arrangement is LNER Class X?

9. What is the name of the NER Class X1 preserved at York?

10. The Great Northern of Scotland Railway owned four dock shunters in Classes Z4 and Z5. Who built them?

11. Which North British engineer designed the Class C16 4-4-2Ts?

12. Did any pre-Grouping LNER companies possess any 4-6-0 tanks?

13. What was the wheel arrangement of the Great Eastern 'Jazz' tanks.

14. The Class G5 tank was an 0-4-4T. True or false?

15. The Great Northern Railway's Class C12s were designed by whom?

Section 59:
BR Standard Pacific Classes

PICTURE QUESTION: In better days, this 'Britannia' hauled 'Golden Arrow' trains on the Southern Region. What name did this locomotive carry?

1. When was the first 'Britannia' Class locomotive delivered?

2. Which region was the first to get a batch of 'Britannias'?

3. Where were the survivors of the class all based in their final years?

4. Where is the officially preserved 'Britannia' kept?

5. Which three 'Britannias' were once allocated to 'Golden Arrow' duties?

6. Which 'Britannia' was never named?

7. Which was 'Britannia' named after a BR Board member?

8. How many cylinders does a 'Britannia' have?

9. What fittings were experimentally fitted to Nos. 70043/4 in the early 1950s?

10. What was the power classification of No. 71000 *Duke of Gloucester*?

11. How many 'Clans' were built?

12. An order for how many additional 'Clans' was cancelled?

13. Apart from Scotland, which region were a second batch of 'Clans' intended for?

14. Where were the first five 'Clans' scrapped in 1963?

15. What was the last surviving 'Clan'?

Section 60:
BR Standard 4-6-0 Classes

PICTURE QUESTION: Between which years were the Standard Class 5 4-6-0s were built?

1. How many Standard Class 5MTs were built?

2. Which works built the Class 5MTs?

3. In which year was new 5MT No. 73000 introduced?

4. Which three 5MTs were built specially for the Somerset & Dorset line?

5. From which locomotives did 20 5MTs take their names?

6. What were their number series?

7. What type of non-standard valve gear was fitted to Nos. 73125-54?

8. Which 5MT is preserved at the Midland Railway Centre?

9. What was the Class 4MT number series?

10. How many Class 4MTs was it was originally intended to build?

11. To which two regions were 4MTs not delivered new?

12. When were the final 4MT withdrawals made?

13. What draughting modification was made to some of the 4MT from 1957?

14. A Class 4MT 4-6-0 is based at Cranmore. What is its name?

15. Where were the design drawings prepared for the 4MTs?

Section 61:
BR Standard 2-6-0 Classes

PICTURE QUESTION: This BR 2-6-0 is shown in dismantled condition on a preserved line. Do you recognise it?

1. In which year was the first Class 4MT 2-6-0 delivered?

2. Upon which LMS number series was the 4MT based?

3. Which region of BR was the last to use Class 4MT 2-6-0s?

4. No. 76114 was the last steam locomotive built at which works?

5. Which preserved Class 4MT has carried the name *Hermes*?

6. The 3MT was a tender version of which BR tank number series?

7. What was the Class 3MT's boiler design number?

8. Where were the Class 3MTs built?

9. Which was the celebrated last survivor of Class 3MT in 1967?

10. An order for an additional how many 3MTs was cancelled?

11. What was the number series of the BR Class 2MT 2-6-0?

12. Which region accepted the first ten 2MTs in 1952?

13. The 2MTs were built at Darlington Works. True or false?

14. Which 2MT is preserved in the town of its birth?

15. Preserved 78022 has been trialled with a Giesl Ejector. Where?

Section 62:
BR Standard 9Fs

PICTURE QUESTION: To which region was the first Class 9F 2-10-0 first allocated?

1. When was the class introduced on BR?

2. Where were the 9Fs built?

3. In which month and year was the last new 9F outshopped?

4. What number is *Evening Star*, the last steam loco built by BR?

5. How many were fitted with mechanical stokers?

6. Which famous painter purchased 92203 *Black Prince* from BR?

7. What was the special fitment on highest numbered 92250?

8. Where was the final depot for the survivors in 1968?

9. Which was first to be fitted with a double chimney?

10. Which example is preserved on the Bluebell Railway?

11. How many were equipped with Franco-Crosti boilers?

12. How many pairs of driving wheels of the 9Fs were flangeless?

13. What diameter are the 9F's driving wheels?

14. Several 9Fs had Westinghouse compressors for ore traffic to which North East steelworks?

15. Which is the oldest preserved 9F?

Section 63:
BR Tank Classes

1. What was the number of the first built Class 4MT tank?

2. Which suburban route displaced large numbers of 800xx tanks as early as 1962?

3. Which was the last locomotive built at Brighton Works in 1957?

4. A Class 4MT tank was the first BR standard locomotive withdrawn in 1962 — what was its number?

5. Preserved 80002 survived as a stationary boiler at which depot?

6. What was the number of the first-built 3MT tank?

7. How many Class 3MT tanks were originally ordered from Swindon?

PICTURE QUESTION: Standard 2-6-4T No. 80135 has been painted in non-standard lined green livery. Where is it now based?

8. How many 3MT tanks were actually built?

9. In which year were the first Class 3MT withdrawals?

10. What were the final duties of the Class 3MT tanks 82019 and 82029?

11. At which works were the 84000 series 2MT tanks built?

12. What number series was the LMS-inspired equivalent?

13. Which enclosed system abandoned plans to take over 2MT tanks in 1965?

14. The 2MT tanks were push-pull fitted. True or false?

15. A replica Class 2MT tank is being assembled at the Bluebell Railway. What number will it carry?

CHAPTER FIVE

Diesel and Electric Locomotives

Section 64:
Diesel Shunters

1. What was the intended purpose of the Andrew Barclay Class 06?

2. What was the role of the final Class 06 No. 06003?

3. What was the number series of the Andrew Barclay 0-6-0?

4. What number did the original member of Class 08 first carry?

5. Where was the first Class 03 built and when?

6. How many traction motors are fitted to the Class 08 design?

7. Which Class 08 has been named *Postman's Pride*?

8. Which Class 08 is preserved at the National Railway Museum?

9. What transmission was fitted to North British designs?

10. Which Class 01 was the first BR shunter sold to industry in 1966?

11. Which company built prototype No. D2999?

12. The first Class 11 shunter was built by which pre-nationalisation company?

13. Which city houses the museum of over 40 BR shunters?

14. Where did Departmental Class 03s Nos. 91 and 92 regularly work?

15. What was the Class designation of the Yorkshire Engine 0-4-0s Nos. D2850-69?

PICTURE QUESTION: This Class 05 survived in BR service two decades beyond the rest of the class. Where?

Section 65:
Class 20

PICTURE QUESTION: Which railway operator has hired last-built Class 20 No. 20227 for long periods since withdrawal from BR service?

1. When did the first Class 20 enter traffic on BR?

2. What was so significant about this date?

3. Where was it built?

4. How many of the prototype series were there?

5. What were the two principal modificatons carried out during the 1980s?

6. What is the number series of the Hunslet-Barclay owned batch?

7. What are they used to haul?

8. What major international construction contract involved the class in the early 1990s?

9. Which example has been retained as a scrapyard shunter in Scotland?

10. What is the name carried by the last-built example No. 20227?

11. What was the TOPs number of first-built Class 20?

12. Which was the first to be built with a headcode panel?

13. A number of Class 20s now work in an EEC country — which one?

14. Which British concern paid to refurbish five Class 20s in 1995?

15. What is their number series?

Section 66:
Classes 24-27

PICTURE QUESTION: Which three regions had Class 27s from new?

1. Which region borrowed a batch of new Class 24 locomotives to steam-heat its trains?

2. What was the power rating of the Class 24?

3. Why were a batch of Class 24s fitted with tripcock signalling apparatus?

4. What were the original duties of Gateshead's Nos. D5096-D5113?

5. Where is the last BR survivor No. 24081 preserved?

6. What was the popular nickname of the Class 25s?

7. Which was the first Class 25 delivered new in blue livery?

8. How many Class 25s were converted to train-heat units?

9. Which Class 25 was known as the 'Ice Cream Van'?

10. What was the last year of regular BR service for Class 25s?

11. Where were the first Class 26s originally allocated?

12. Where was the factory that built the Class 26s and 27s?

13. What was the principal modification made to the original seven Class 26s ?

14. Where did the push-pull Class 27s originally operate?

15. Where is the pioneer Class 27 kept?

Section 67:
Class 31

PICTURE QUESTION: Class 31 No. 31148 undergoes ETH conversion in 1984 — at which works were all the major overhauls conducted during its long career?

1. In what month and year did No. D5500 make its passenger debut?

2. What is the Class 31 wheel arrangement?

3. What was the nickname of the original batch?

4. Where was the first batch allocated?

5. In what livery was No. D5579 experimentally painted?

6. Who built the original power units and what was their power rating?

7. Which locomotive was trialled in the north of Scotland during 1958?

8. Which Class 31 was trialled with an uprated 2000 bhp engine?

9. Which was the first Class 31 to be withdrawn, and when?

10. Which LM London depot had a small allocation of 31/4s in the early 1970s?

11. Which preserved line used the officially-preserved No. D5500 during 1996?

12. How many Class 31s were converted for electric train heating?

13. Which was the first Class 31 to be named?

14. What is the unofficial name of the now-preserved No. 31418?

15. What is the highest TOPS number ever carried by a Class 31?

Section 68:
Class 33 'Cromptons'

PICTURE QUESTION: The original purpose of the push-pull Class 33/1 was to provide power for which type of Southern Region passenger unit west of Bournemouth?

1. How many Class 33s were built?

2. What principal equipment on the locomotive carries the 'Crompton' name?

3. Which main works undertook their overhauls?

4. Which example was withdrawn in 1964 after a collision?

5. Which was repainted green during the 1980s for prestige duties?

6 How many were push-pull fitted?

7. What was the original class designation for Class 33/1, never adopted?

8. Which line were the narrow-bodied series built for?

9. What was their other special characteristic?

10. Which two Class 33s hauled Lord Mountbatten's funeral train in 1979?

11. Which two Class 33s have carried the names *The Burma Star*?

12. How many cylinders does the Class 33 Sulzer power unit have?

13. What is the power unit's output in brake horse power?

14. Only one push-pull Class 33/1 ran in green livery. Which was it?

15. Which pair of Class 33s visited Inverness on a railtour in 1995?

Section 69:
Class 35 'Hymeks'

PICTURE QUESTION: Which Class 35 'Hymek' carried this grey and yellow livery for a short time from 1992?

1. How many 'Hymeks' were constructed?

2. Which region employed them?

3. What was their number series?

4. What was their power type designation?

5. Which private contractor constructed them, and where?

6. What type of engine was installed?

7. What did the contrived name 'Hymek' signify?

8. What was the multiple working symbol they allocated?

9. Main overhauls of the class were undertaken at Swindon Works. True or false?

10. During which year did the first withdrawals take place?

11. Which famous incline employed Class 35s in multiple as banking engines?

12. Which 'Hymeks' were retained for dead-load trials?

13. Where were they kept?

14. Which preserved line has two 'Hymeks' based there?

15. Which preserved 'Hymek' has the same number as a 'Castle' Class steam locomotive?

Section 70:
Class 37

PICTURE QUESTION: The current No. 37271 is the second Class 37 to carry this number. What other numbers has it carried?

1. What was the original identity of the first class member?

2. What is its current number?

3. What is the Class 37 wheel arrangement?

4. Which locomotive was destroyed in the 1965 Bridgend collision?

5. How many Class 37s were rebuilt with on-board electric train equipment?

6. At which works was refurbishment carried out on many of the class in the 1980s?

7. How many Class 37s were fitted with split headcode panels?

8. Which Region had the initial allocation from 1961?

9. Which two Class 37s took part in the WR's 1965 high-speed trials?

10. What was the main generator replaced with during refurbishment?

11. What is the sub-class designation of those used on Channel Tunnel night trains?

12. What two types of engine are fitted to the Class 37/9 sub-class?

13. Which three Class 37s were named for only a few weeks in 1963?

14. What was the livery applied to No. 37093 for a TV advertisement?

15. Which Class 37/4 has different names on each side?

Section 71:
Class 40

1. To which two depots were the pilot series Nos. D200-9 first allocated?

2. In what year did the first Class 40 enter service?

3. What was the class's popular nickname in the 1980s?

4. Which Class 40 was written-off in an accident in 1966?

5. What was the final number of the first-built Class 40?

6. Which depot undertook its restoration to working order?

7. Which was the first to be built with centre headcode panels?

8. Where is this locomotive now preserved?

9. How many horsepower was the EE power unit?

10. Which Class 40 was involved in the 1963 Great Train Robbery?

11. How many were built with nose-end doors and marker lamp discs?

12. Where was the track reconstruction project that saw four Class 40s reinstated for department service in 1985?

13. How many Class 40s were fitted with ETH equipment?

14. Which North East builder assembled 20 of the class in 1960/61?

15. What was the purported name of No. D226, not believed carried?

PICTURE QUESTION: How many Class 40s were named by BR like this one, No. 212 *Aureol*?

Section 72:
Class 41-43 'Warships'

PICTURE QUESTION: This preserved 'Warship' was pictured while in store at Swindon Works in 1981. Can you identify it?

1. Which private builder assembled Nos. D600-D604?

2. Who designed the Class 41's power units?

3. What was the Class 41's final depot?

4. How many Class 41s received blue livery?

5. Which Class 41 survived at Barry into the 1980s?

6. What was the name of the first-built Class 42 No. D800?

7. What was the intended name for No. D812, but not carried?

8. What emblem carried on the cabside of No. D823 *Hermes*?

9. In what month and year were the last examples withdrawn by BR?

10. Which example survived 13 years before being scrapped in 1985?

11. Which 'Warship' was experimentally fitted with Paxman engines?

12. Were the 'Warships' classified Type 3 or Type 4?

13. How Class 43 'Warships' many were built in Glasgow?

14. In what year were the first Class 43 withdrawals?

15. How many Class 43s are preserved?

Section 73:
Class 44-46 'Peaks'

PICTURE QUESTION: Main line-registered No. D172 *Ixion* was a former test locomotive — what was its departmental number?

1. What was the name of the first Class 44 'Peak' locomotive?

2. Where were the first 'Peak' Sulzer engines built?

3. Which early series 'Peak' had its engine uprated for tests?

4. Which Class 44 was first preserved in Scotland, and what was its later name?

5. What was the Class 44s' final allocation base?

6. What is the wheel arrangement of all 'Peaks'?

7. How many Class 45s carried nose-end doors from new?

8. In what year was the final Class 45 delivered?

9. Which was the only Class 45 not named after a regiment?

10. What was the five-figure TOPS number of Sherwood Forester?

11. How many Class 46s were built?

12. The Class 46 traction motors were different — who made them?

13. What name was applied to the test locomotive No. 97403?

14. At which works were large numbers of redundant Class 46s temporarily stored from 1980?

15. Where was No. 46026 *Leicestershire & Derbyshire Yeomanry* scrapped and when?

Section 74:
Classes 47 and 48

PICTURE QUESTION: 'Provincial' livery was applied to this Class 47 No. 47475 for a short time — how many more carried this paint style?

1. Where the first series of Class 47s built?

2. Which BR works built the rest?

3. How many Class 47s and 48s were finally constructed?

4. What is the standard power unit designation?

5. What was the principal difference of No. D1702-6?

6. Which Class 47 was renumbered because of superstition?

7. Which Class 47 carried a nameplate beginning with the letter X?

8. Where was No. D1671 written off in an accident in 1965?

9. Which was the first locomotive to carry BR blue livery?

10. Where is the first-built Class 47 preserved?

11. How many Class 47s were converted to push-pull operation for Scotland?

12. Which depot has been the base of Res-owned Class 47s?

13. What is the maximum speed of parcels-dedicated Class 47s?

14. What was the name of Tinsley's flagship Class 47 No. 47145?

15. What numbers did the Ruston-engined prototype carry through its career?

Section 75:
Class 50

PICTURE QUESTION: Which main line route was the final home for the Class 50s, and who owns No. 50033 *Glorious* now?

1. How many Class 50s were built?

2. During which two years were all 50 Class 50s delivered?

3. Upon which prototype was the design based?

4. How many were originally steam-heat boiler fitted?

5. What was the coupling code of the Class 50s?

6. Which Class 50 was repainted in GWR green livery in 1985?

7. What was its original name?

8. Which Class 50 is preserved by the National Railway Museum?

9. Which Class 50 was badly damaged at Paddington in 1984?

10 Which depot was the original home of the Class 50s?

11. Which was the first to enter service on the Western Region, and when?

12. Which works carried out total refurbishment from 1979 onwards?

13. What was the principal modification carried out to No. 50049 for it to become 50149?

14. What was the class's maximum speed when new?

15. Which Class 50 was moved to Scotland in 1995 for preservation?

Section 76:
Class 52 'Westerns'

1. What livery was carried by the first-built Class 52?

2. What colour paint scheme was applied to second-of-the-class No. D1001 *Western Pathfinder*?

3. How many brake horsepower did the two Maybach power units generate inside a 'Western'?

4. What was the first allocation for the Class 52?

5. What was the final allocation for the class?

6. Only one Class 52 was equipped with nose-end marker lights in BR service. Which was it?

7. How many Class 52 'Westerns' were built at Crewe Works?

8. Which was the first Class 52 withdrawal?

9. Which pair of 'Westerns' hauled the farewell BR excursion train in February 1977?

10. Which Class 52 carried a mis-spelt nameplate for many years?

11. Name the BR works that both overhauled and scrapped the entire class.

12. In what year did major overhauls cease on Class 52s?

13. Which was the very first Class 52 'Western' to be reserved for a preservation society?

14. What was the final regular freight duty for the Class 52s before their withdrawal?

15. Which BR prototype diesel-electric locomotive was fitted with similar Maybach engines?

PICTURE QUESTION: What was externally unique about Class 52 No. D1015?

Section 77:
Class 55 'Deltics'

PICTURE QUESTION: What front end 'Deltic' experiment was uniquely trialled by No. D9000 in the early 1960s?

1. Which three depots had the original allocations?

2. What was the design weight of the Class 55?

3. Which was the first 'Deltic' to be scrapped?

4. When was the NRM's No 55002 repainted green?

5. Which was the first 'Deltic' to be overhauled and painted blue?

6. How many cylinders has each 'Deltic' power unit?

7. What front end livery modification was applied to the London-based series in the early 1980s?

8. Which locomotives were loaned to the WR for high speed trials in 1975?

9. Cabs were purchased from which two 'Deltics' after their scrapping?

10. How many examples are preserved?

11. What was the combined horsepower of the power units in each locomotive?

12. How many Class 55s were named after racehorses?

13. On what date did *Royal Scots Grey* make its final BR run?

14. Which was the first 'Deltic' to cover two million miles in 1973?

15. Which Class 55 took part in the 1980 Rainhill cavalcade?

Section 78:
Classes 56-60

PICTURE QUESTION: Class 56 No. 56062 is named after a quarry — in which county is Mountsorrel?

1. Where were the original series of 30 Class 56s assembled— Romania or Russia?

2. What is the number of the first British-built Class 56?

3. Which Class 56 locomotive pioneeredthe use of 'large logo' livery?

4. Where were the final batch of Class 56s built?

5. Which Class 56 was the first to be withdrawn and when?

6. How many Class 58s are there?

7. Where were the Class 58s built, and between which years?

8. How many Class 58s have train heating capability?

9. Which Class 58 is named *Toton Traction Depot*?

10. In which year did the first Class 59 arrive in the UK?

11. How many Class 59s were in traffic at the beginning of 1996?

12. What is the brake horsepower of a Class 59?

13. Which British engineering firm assembled the Class 60?

14. What is the Class 60's wheel arrangement?

15. What is the maximum speed of a Class 60 locomotive?

Section 79:
Classes 71-77

PICTURE QUESTION: Class 73 No. 73101 is unique in carrying Pullman-style livery. What was its name before it become *The Royal Alex*?

1. What was the number of the first-built Class 71 electric?

2. Which service requires a dedidcated fleet of 12 Class 73s?

3. What hrsepower of the Class 73 diesel engine?

4. Which Class 73 hauled the Royal Wedding train in 1981?

5. What number was temporarily applied to the first-built Class 73 in July 1989?

6. What livery was applied to No. 73133 in 1996?

7. Which famous CME is honoured by nameplates on No. 73128?

8. Which northern depot acquired Class 73/0s for departmental service?

9. How many Class 71s were converted to Class 74, and where was the work done?

10. Where did the original Class 76 No. 6701 run trials between 1947-52?

11. Which running shed maintained the Class 76s?

12. Why were the Class 76s withdrawn en masse in 1981?

13. How many Class 77 (EM2) were built?

14. What livery did they originally carry in BR service from 1953?

15. Which Class 77 is preserved near Rotterdam?

Section 80:
Classes 81-92

PICTURE QUESTION: Class 86 No. 86401 was unique in carrying Network SouthEast livery. What was its name at the time?

1. When was the pioneer Class 81 AC electric new?

2. What was its original and final number?

3. How many AEI/Beyer Peacock Class 82s were built?

4. What was unique about the last built Class 83 No. E3100?

5. Which locomotive company built the National Railway Museum's Class 84 No. 84001?

6. What is the number of the sole-surviving Class 85?

7. What have the Class 86s *City of Milton Keynes*, *The Times* and *L.S. Lowry* have in common?

8. How many Class 86s were reconstructed with bogies similiar to those fitted to Class 87s?

9. Freight-owned Class 86s belong to which sub-class?

10. Class 87 No. 87001 has carried two names in its career — what are they?

11. The Class 89's wheel arrangement is unique for a British AC locomotive — what is it?

12. Which five Class 90s are owned by the parcels business?

13. What is the design speed for a Class 91?

14. What is the horse power rating for a Class 91?

15. Who are the owners of the new Class 92s?

CHAPTER SIX

Match The Name

Section 81:
LNER Steam Names

PICTURE QUESTION: *Cuddie Headrigg* — which locomotive carried this name?

Match the locomotive number with the name:

1. 60021	A. *Lord Faringdon*
2. 61700	B. *Dante*
3. 60847	C. *Flying Scotsman*
4. 61000	D. *Bantam Cock*
5. 61250	E. *Minoru*
6. 60062	F. *Loch Arkaig*
7. 60014	G. *Springbok*
8. 60145	H. *Wolf of Badenoch*
9. 60034	I. *Sandringham*
10. 61600	J. *The Durham Light Infantry*
11. 61633	K. *Wild Swan*
12. 61764	L. *Silver Link*
13. 62277	M. *Gordon Highlander*
14. 62760	N. *Andrew K. McKosh*
15. 60513	O. *St Peter's School York, AD627*
16. 60003	P. *Kimbolton Castle*
17. 60506	Q. *Saint Mungo*
18. 60964	R. *A. Harold Bibby*
19. 61997	S. *MacCailin Mor*
20. 60103	T. *The Cotswold*

Section 82:
LMS Steam Names

PICTURE QUESTION: *City of Coventry's* name and numberplate adorn the stairway of which station?

Match the locomotive number with the name:

1. 45556		A. *City of Carlisle*
2. 46102		B. *Comet*
3. 54767		C. *Nova Scotia*
4. 45647		D. *City of London*
5. 46128		E. *Black Watch*
6. 46212		F. *The Manchester Regiment*
7. 46245		G. *Rooke*
8. 45158		H. *Sturdee*
9. 45581		I. *Royal Scots Grey*
10. 46125		J. *3rd Carabinier*
11. 46204		K. *Queen Mary*
12. 46238		L. *Glasgow Yeomanry*
13. 54398		M. *Princess Arthur of Connaught*
14. 45699		N. *Galatea*
15. 46101		O. *Clan Mackinnon*
16. 46148		P. *Ben Alder*
17. 46222		Q. *Bihar and Orissa*
18. 45511		R. *The Lovat Scouts*
19. 45500		S. *Ben Clebrig*
20. 45660		

Section 83:
SR Steam Names

PICTURE QUESTION: *Channel Packet's* nameplate now adornes a wall at the National Railway Museum, York. It was the first Bulleid Pacific — what was its BR number?

Match the locomotive number with the name:

1. 30453	A. *Biggin Hill*
2. 34001	B. *Beachey Head*
3. 32424	C. *King Arthur*
4. W14	D. *Fighter Command*
5. 32333	E. *Calbourne*
6. 35030	F. *Elder Dempster Lines*
7. 34016	G. *Exeter*
8. 30799	H. *Port Line*
9. 34057	I. *Lord Nelson*
10. 30926	J. *Fishbourne*
11. 30949	K. *Callington*
12. 30768	L. *A.S. Harris*
13. 34047	M. *145 Squadron*
14. 35027	N *Bodmin*
15. 30451	O. *Repton*
16. W24	P. *Remembrance*
17. 30756	Q. *Sir Balin*
18. 30850	R. *Sir Lamorak*
19. 34087	S. *Sir Ironside*
20. 34064	T. *Hecate*

Section 84:
GWR Steam Names

Match the locomotive number with the name:

1. 5042		A. *King Edward I*
2. 6024		B. *G.J. Churchward*
3. 7800		C. *Hinderton Hall*
4. 6879		D. *Torquay Manor*
5. 4900		E. *Albert Hall*
6. 4073		F. *Frilsham Manor*
7. 5900		G. *Toddington Grange*
8. 4930		H. *Hagley Hall*
9. 7827		I. *Overton Grange*
10. 1011		J. *Thornbury Castle*
11. 4015		K. *Saint Martin*
12. 7017		L. *Knight of St John*
13. 1000		M *Windsor Castle*
14. 4983		N *Caerphilly Castle*
15. 6967		O. *Willesley Hall*
16. 7027		P. *Peatling Hall*
17. 4082		Q. *Lydham Manor*
18. 7816		R. *County of Middlesex*
19. 6848		S. *Winchester Castle*
20. 6959		T. *County of Chester*

**PICTURE QUESTION: The nameplate from GWR 4-6-0
Kingsway Hall — what was its number?**

Section 85:
BR Steam Names

PICTURE QUESTION: Standard 'Pacific' *Britannia* shares its name with which Class 87 electric?

Match the locomotive number with the name:

1. 70006	A. *Shooting Star*
2. 92220	B. *North British*
3. 72000	C. *Rudyard Kipling*
4. 90732	D. *Robert Burns*
5. 70045	E. *Tintagel*
6. 73084	F. *Oliver Cromwell*
7. 70041	G. *King Leodegrance*
8. 70019	H. *Moray Firth*
9. 70053	I *Vulcan*
10. 90773	J. *William Wordsworth*
11. 70035	K. *Clan Buchanan*
12. 72009	L. *Lightning*
13. 70030	M. *Duke of Gloucester*
14. 73086	N. *The Green Knight*
15. 70036	O. *Evening Star*
16. 70013	P. *Sir John Moore*
17. 73082	Q. *Lord Rowallan*
18. 71000	R. *Clan Stewart*
19. 73118	S. *Camelot*
20. 70029	T. *Boadicea*

Section 86:
BR Diesel Names

PICTURE QUESTION: Which Class 60 locomotive has ben named *Steadfast*?

Match the locomotive number with the correct name:

1. 59005	A. *Mauretania*
2. 44010	B. *Grenadier Guardsman*
3. 08994	C. *Western Viscount*
4. 40011	D. *Kenneth J. Painter*
5. D842	E. *Western Bulwark*
6. 55007	F. *Lion*
7. 37403	G. *Merehead*
8. D1073	H. *Tryfan*
9. 47401	I. *Western Pathfinder*
10. D818	J. *Ben Cruachan*
11. 56031	K. *Lusitania*
12. D833	L. *North Eastern*
13. 33116	M. *Boar of Badenoch*
14. 50027	N. *Gwendraeth*
15. D1001	O. *Glory*
16. 45111	P. *Hertfordshire Railtours*
17. D870	Q. *Zulu*
18. 40025	R. *Pinza*
19. 60100	S. *Panther*
20. D1045	T. *Royal Oak*

Section 87:
BR Electric Names

PICTURE QUESTION: Class 91 No. 91007 is named after a famous railway enthusiast — who is he?

Match the locomotive number with the correct name:

1. 90009	A. *Sir Herbert Walker*
2. 86204	B. *Robert A. Riddles*
3. 92001	C. *Queen Elizabeth II*
4. 73119	D. *Swallow*
5. 27004	E. *Iron Duke*
6. 86611	F. *The Economist*
7. 90019	G. *Juno*
8. 87005	H. *Penny Black*
9. 86245	I. *Vrachtverbinding*
10. 73003	J. *Victor Hugo*
11. 91029	K. *Pebble Mill*
12. 76051	L. *City of Carlisle*
13. 91001	M. *City of London*
14. 86256	N. *Vaughan Williams*
15. 86102	O. *Mentor*
16. 92041	P. *Kentish Mercury*
17. 87017	Q. *Aldaniti*
18. 76057	R. *Dudley Castle*
19. 90128	S. *Ulysees*
20. 86628	T. *Airey Neave*

CHAPTER SEVEN

Foreign Railways

Section 88:
Overseas Railways

PICTURE QUESTION: This preserved American-built 141R 2-8-2 was designed for which European country?

Ireland

1. What is the name of the main locomotive works in Dublin?
2. Which town has the railway terminus for sea services to Stranraer?
3. What are the names of the two stations at each end of the main inter-city route?
4. By what name is the Dublin electrified suburban system known?
5. Which American builder has supplied large number of locomotives to Irish Railways since the 1970s?

Germany

6. What does the German word *Hauptbahnhof* mean?
7. What voltage is the standard for most of the German electrified network?
8. In which year did the DB dispense with steam power?
9. What two colours make up the livery of the ICE high-speed units?
10. What is a 'Köf'?

Portugal

11. Which two letters are used as the short form for Compania dos Caminhos de Ferro Portugueses?
12. The Estoril Railway travels along the coastline on the outskirts of which city?
13. What is the track gauge for main lines in Portugal?
14. What is the name of the principal locomotive repair works in Lisbon?
15. The Portuguese 1400 Class of locomotive is based on the British Class 50. True or false?

Section 89:
Overseas Railways

PICTURE QUESTION: The BB 8500 Class is the dc version of which similar French electric design?

Austria

1. How many management divisions comprise Austria Railways?
2. What name is given to the fast Inter-City services?
3. What is the wheel designation of the 1926-built Class 1180 electric locomotives?
4. Austrian Railways staged a major anniversary exhibition in 1987. How many years of existence was it celebrating?
5. In which country were the Class 1043 thyristor controlled electric locomotives built?

France

6. What are the letters TGV short for?
7. From which Paris station do trains leave for the Channel Tunnel?
8. In which town is the French national railway museum?
9. Shunting locomotive numbers are prefixed by which letter?
10. Diesel locomotives of which class are known as 'Baldwins'?

Netherlands

11. What is the Dutch name for Netherlands Railways?
12. The principal locomotive maintenance centre is at Tilburg. True or false?
13. To which Western European country were 2400 Class diesel locomotives sold in 1990?
14. Which class of electric locomotive, built 1951-3, sports an American appearance?
15. What is the nickname of the celebrity VIP diesel saloon?

Section 90:
Overseas Railways

PICTURE QUESTION: The British English Electric Class 50 design was modified for use in which country? How many were exported?

Belgium

1. The initials NMBS and SNCB are both used to Belgian Railways. Which is the French and which is the Flemish version?
2. Electric locomotives Nos. 1501-5 were purchased from British Rail in 1969. True or false?
3. Where are two main workshops for overhauling rolling stock?
4. Which class of dual-voltage locomotives are used on the Brussels-Amsterdam Inter-City push-pull services?
5. What colours form the principal livery of the main line diesel locomotive fleet?

Spain

6. What does RENFE stand for?
7. What are the three principal track gauges used in Spain?
8. What is the name of the Spanish ultra-lightweight articulated train?
9. Where is the southernmost Spanish railway centre?
10. In which year was the Madrid-Seville high speed line opened?

Switzerland

11. Which three sets of three letters are used by Swiss Railways as its initials?
12. Name the three divisions of Swiss Railways?
13. What class does lowest-numbered Bo-Bo locomotive No. 10001 belong?
14. What is the name of the company operating services through the Lötschberg Tunnel?
15. Where is the Sulzer locomotive works based?

Section 91:
Overseas Locations

Can you identify which European countries these views belong to?

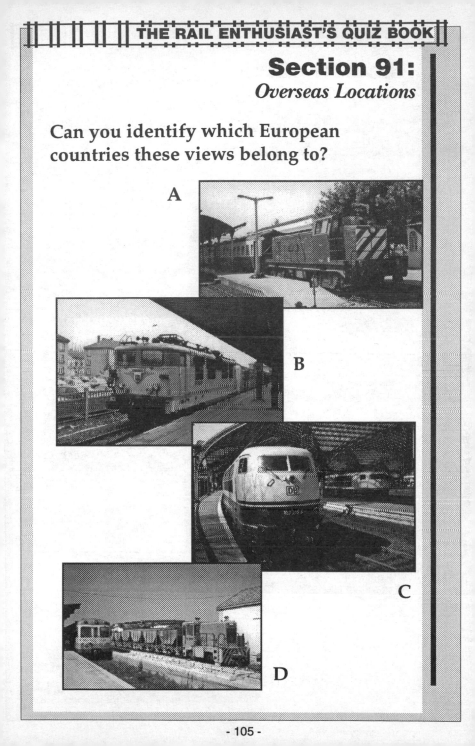

A

B

C

D

Section 92:
Overseas Locations

Can you identify which European countries these views belong to?

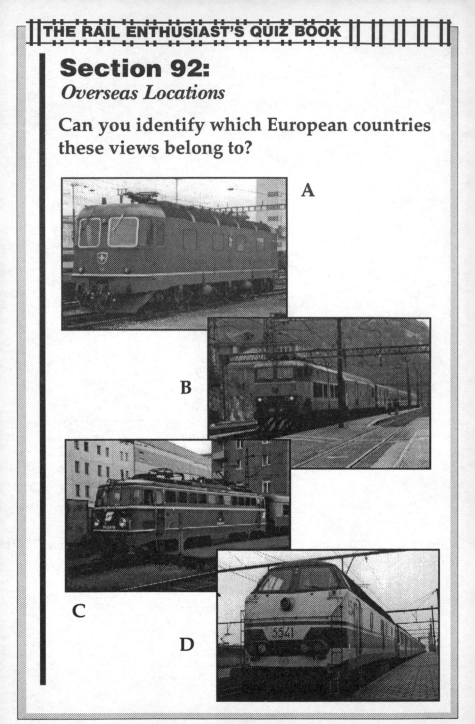

A

B

C

D

CHAPTER EIGHT

Preservation

Section 93:
Preservation

Picture Question: Caledonian Railway No. 419 dates back to 1908. Where was it built, and what was the LMS power classification?

1. Where is the northern terminus of the KWVR?

2. Where is the headquarters of the preserved line through the Churnet Valley?

3. Which entrepreneur inspired the building of the Kent & East Sussex Railway?

4. Which company operated the Bluebell Line until 1923?

5. Where has the original Haymarket train shed from Edinburgh has been re-erected?

6. Where is the home of Stanier 4-6-2 No. 46235 City of Birmingham?

7. Which station is the main centre of the Yorkshire Dales Railway?

8. Which was British Railway's last-steam operated line?

9. Which line is associated with the artist David Shepherd?

10. What is the route length of the North Yorkshire Moors Railway between Pickering and Grosmont?

11. The South Tynedale Railway operates a narrow gauge line on the trackbed of which ex-BR route?

12. Ramsbottom is an intermediate station on which line?

13. Where is the home of the Great Western Society?

14. The North Norfolk Railway runs over the track of which pre-Grouping company?

15. Which railway museum is next to the Meadowhall shopping centre at Sheffield?

Section 94:
Preservation

Picture Question: LNWR tank No. 1054 took part in a famous locomotive cavalcade in 1980. Where was it?

1. If Peak Rail achieves its objectives, which stations will it run between?

2. Which former Cheltenham station will be used by the Gloucestershire Warwickshire Railway?

3. The Birmingham Railway Museum occupies the site of a former main line steam depot. Where?

4. In which year was the West Somerset Railway re-opened?

5. Which rail has a main line connection at Smallbrook Junction?

6. Boat of Garten is the main base of which Scottish preserved line?

7. Where does the rolling stock owned by Derby Corporation reside?

8. Which Devon seaside railway shares the same location with incoming High Speed Trains?

9. The Great Central Railway can only re-open its full length when a bridge is built - where?

10. Which city does the Nene Valley Railway run into?

11. To which lake does the Lakeside & Haverthwaite convey passengers?

12. Which preserved line occupies a section of the Midland, South Western & Junction Railway?

13. Where is Metropolitan Railway No. 23 kept?

14. Which Devon preserved branch terminus was lost because of road widening on the approaches?

15. The Appleby Frodingham RPS operates within which East Midlands steelworks?

Section 95:
Preservation

Picture Question: Which preserved railway was the first home for this Class 44 diesel No. 44008, and what was its temporary name?

1. Which preservation site has the former BR depot code 81C?

2. Which Fifeshire railway, now closed, was the original home of Class A4 4-6-2 No. 60009 Union of South Africa?

3. What gauge is the Romney, Hythe & Dymchurch Railway?

4. The Middleton Railway operates on the outskirts of which city?

5. Which 2ft 6in gauge preserved railway was built to serve paper mills in North Kent?

6. The Severn Valley Railway re-opened to passengers in 1970. True or false?

7. The Llangollen Railway was operated by the Cambrian Railway. True or false?

8. The Seaton branch is now relaid as a tramway between which two locations?

9. Which preservation centre boasts an original coaling tower next to the West Coast Main Line?

10. In which county is the Ravenglass & Eskdale Railway?

11. What was the final BR shed code for Southport?

12. At what height is the summit station of the Snowdon Mountain Railway?

13. Which famous ruined monument forms a backdrop for the Swanage Railway?

14. The Caledonian Railway is based in which Scottish town?

15. Where was the Bulmer Railway Centre?

Section 96:
Preservation

1. LSWR Class T9 4-4-0 No. 120 is known by what nickname?

2. Which now closed Yorkshire line employed a pair of Class 04s Nos. D2245 and D2298?

3. LNWR 0-6-2T was known as what?

4. The Swanage Railway's tank No. 30075 was built in which country?

5. The ex-Network SouthEast tube-size coach at the National Railway Museum belonged to which line?

6. The sole-preserved Glasgow & South Western Railway is of what wheel arrangement?

7. Class 28 No. D5705 has what design of power unit?

8. The TOPS number of Class 31 was 31001. True or false?

9. The USA design 2-8-0s running in Britain are from which class?

10. What is the number of the Stanier 8F 2-6-0 rescued from Turkey?

11. What gauge is replica steam locomotive Iron Duke?

12. What is the name of Class 40 No. D306?

13. Who was the first private owner of Flying Scotsman?

14. LNER Class N7 No. 69621 sometimes carries the name of its designer. Who was he?

15. A GWR-design 0-6-0PT was once plinthed outside a hotel in which city?

Picture Question: Caledonian 4-2-2 No. 123 was used on many specials in the 1960s. Where is it preserved now?

Section 97:
Preserved locomotives

Picture Question: Which foreign countries was Flying Scotsman shipped to in 1989, and which British locomotive was it reunited with?

1. What is the name carried in preservation by No. 44871?

2. What did the initials SLOA stand for?

3. Where are Stanier Pacifics Nos. 46201 and 46203 now based?

4. What was the original number of Class 50 No. 50050?

5. Electric locomotive Ariadne is preserved at which city museum?

6. Where do two Class 52 'Westerns' operate together?

7. Prototype diesel shunters Tom and Tiger were built by which company?

8. The 'Ice Cream Van' Class 25 was officially named just prior to withdrawal. What was it?

9. What is the LNER class number of 0-6-0 No. 1217E at the National Railway Museum?

10. Which GWR 0-6-0PT ended its working days at Mountain Ash Colliery in the mid-1970s?

11. What is the name of Class D49 4-4-0 No. 246 preserved at Bo'ness?

12. How many Class 09 diesel shunters are preserved?

13. Class 02 Calbourne on the Isle of Wight is an 0-4-4T. True or false?

14. What gauge is Tiny, preserved at the South Devon Railway?

15. What was the Eastern Region departmental number of LNER Class B1 No. 1264?

CHAPTER NINE

The Final Word

Section 98:
Anagrams

PICTURE QUESTION: Can you identify this coach and the location?

Unscramble the following anagrams of principal London stations:

1. Bleary Omen
2. Rings Socks
3. God and Pint
4. Old or Bending
5. Tone Us

6. Traps Cans
7. Ants on Centre
8. Tear Wool
9. I to Vicar
10. Lovelier Protest

11. Lark Fabrics
12. Ten Acorn Nets
13. Earn Contents
14. Motor Age
15. Pining Alto Monkeys

16. No Grand Fir
17. Unjam Lip on Catch
18. Spiky Barn Fur
19. A Log Spoke
20. Led to Rest

Section 99:
Anagrams

PICTURE QUESTION: Do you recognise the entrance to this somewhat remote London depot?

Unscramble the following anagrams of currently operational UK motive power depots:

1. Not To
2. Look Commando
3. Hello Mr Wet
4. Rake My Hat
5. No Taller

6. Real Nod
7. Dines Well
8. Cart and Coffin
9. Light Song
10. King Lent Toy

11. No Gun Breeds
12. Ten No Wheat
13. Western Atlas
14. Dart Forts
15. Slender Age

16. A Rail
17. Never Sins
18. This Eagle
19. Paid Mole
20. Not Sacred

Section 100:
True or False?

PICTURE QUESTION: 'Thomas the Tank Engine' was created by the Rev Wilfred Awdry. True or false?

Are the following statements true or false?

1. The dedicated 'Gatwick Express' service runs out of London Victoria.

2. The Lancashire & Yorkshire's main locomotive works was at Earlestown.

3. BR Garratt locomotive No. 69999 belonged to Class U1.

4. The GWR's gas turbine locomotive No. 18000 was designed in France.

5. The Colne Valley & Halstead Railway was incorporated into the LNER.

6. The BR depot code for Haymarket was 64B.

7. Woodford Halse was on the Great Central Railway.

8. The experimental Fell diesel locomotive was numbered 10101.

9. Dr Beeching was a former chairman of the National Coal Board.

10. The GWR 4200 Class was a 2-8-0T.

11. Preserved No. 49 *Gordon Highlander* was a product of the North British Railway.

12. Westinghouse brake equipment was devised by George Westinghouse.

13. The Manchester-Bury route was once electrified with a 1200v DC third rail.

14. No. 73171 was the last BR standard locomotive built at Wolverton.

15. BR Standard 4-6-0 No. 73110 was named *The Dark Knight*.

CHAPTER TEN

Section 1, True or False? 1. False — Ystrad Rhondda, 2. False — Charles Francis Brush, 3. True, 4. True, 5. True, 6. False — Norwich-Ely line, 7. False — there are no electric-heat Class 56s, 8. True — 61011, 9. True, 10. True, 11. False — City of Chester (Preston is not a city), 12. True, 13. True, 14. True, 15. False. **Picture:** Bath (Green Park).

Section 2, True or False? 1. True, 2. False — Waterloo, 3. False — North and South, 4. True, 5. True, 6. False — Vic Berry, 7. True, 8. True, 9. False — Needham Market, 10. False — Flitwick, 11. True, 12. False — it was 70049, 13. True, 14. False — Bugle, 15. True. **Picture:** Great Northern Railway, Skegness.

Section 3, Dates. 1. 1948, 2. 1963, 3. Swindon, 4. January 1969, 5. January 2 1982, 6. 1986, 7. 1859, 8. 1963, 9. 1975, 10. False, 1825, 11. 1921, 12. 1980, 13. 1933, 14. 1974, 15. 1955. **Picture:** Forth Bridge.

Section 4, Dates. 1. July 1967, 2. 1980, 3. 1935, 4. 1951, 5. October 1952, 6. 1972, 7. August 1968, 8. 1904, 9. March 1966, 10. 1989, 11.Modern Railways, 12. 1895, 13. 1892, 14. 1941, 15. 1972. **Picture:** 1994.

Section 5, Facts and Feats. 1. D600, 2. 'The Decapod', 3. Chimney and exhaust system, 4. 4-6-4T, 5. Dr Rudolph Diesel (1858-1913), 6. 4-6-0, GT3, 7. 1955, 8. False — it is a rack railway, 9. Morecambe and Heysham, 10. The standard card railway ticket, 11. True, 12. LMS, 7850, 13. Volk's Electric Railway, Brighton, 14. 8,298, 15. D4157 (08927). **Picture:** 1986.

Section 6, Facts and Feats. 1. Druimuachdar (1,484ft), 2. Severn Tunnel (144ft below sea level), 3. True, 4. St Pancras (240ft), 5. Highland Railway, 6. 10000, 7. Four, 8. True, 9. Pandrol, 10. 1933, 11. Between Barlby and Brough (Selby-Hull line), 18 miles, 12. Railway timetable, 13. 'Big Boys', 14. Corrour (1,347ft), 15. Metropolitan-Cammell. **Picture:** Finsbury Park, Gateshead, and Haymarket.

Section 7, Famous people. 1. Isambard Kingdom Brunel, 2. Chairman, LNER, 1938-48, 3. George Stephenson, 4. Great Central, 5. True, 6. Belgian, 7. George Hudson, 8. The Queen Mother, 9. Great Western Railway, 10. Andre Chapelon, 11. Italian, 12. Robert Fairlie, 13. Thomas Cook, 14. Gerard Fiennes, 15. John Aspinall. **Picture:** Sir William Stanier.

Section 8, Famous people. 1. Great Northern, 2. North London, 3. Great Eastern, 4. London, Brighton & South Coast, 5. Great Central, 6. North British, 7. Lancashire & Yorkshire, 8. Midland, 9. Great Western, 10. Glasgow & South Western, 11. Lancashire & Yorkshire, 12. London & North Western, 13. Great North of Scotland, 14. North Eastern, 15. Midland & Great Northern, 16. South Eastern & Chatham, 17. London & South Western, 18. Great Western, 19. North Eastern, 20. Great Northern. **Picture**: General Manager, Southern Railway.

Section 9, Nicknames. 1. Great Western Railway, 2. London, Brighton & South Coast, 3. London & North Western, 4. Midland & Great Northern, 5. Somerset & Dorset, 6. Manchester, Sheffield & Lincolnshire, 7. Midland & South Western Junction, 8. Great Northern, 9. London Midland & Scottish, 10. Great Central,

11. London, Chatham & Dover, 12. Manchester, Sheffield & Lincolnshire, 13. London, Midland & Scottish, 14. Manchester, Sheffield & Lincolnshire, 15. Stratford & Midland Junction Railway. **Picture:** 15 Guineas.

Section 10, Nicknames. 1. LMS Class 5 4-6-0, 2. LNER Class O1/O2 2-8-0, 3. LMS Ivatt 2-6-0 and 2-6-2T, 4. BR Class 47, 5. LNER Class A4 4-6-2, 6. BR Class 33/2, 7. L&Y 2-4-2T, 8. Great Central 4-4-2, 9. LNER Class J11 0-6-0, 10. BR Class 37, 11. GNR 0-8-0, 12. BR Class 14, 13. LNER Class K3 2-6-0, 14. LMS Class 6P5F 2-6-0, 15. BR Class 20. **Picture:** The 50th anniversary of the 126mph record speed run by A4 Class 4-6-2 No. 4468 *Mallard*.

Section 11, Anagrams. 1. Swindon, 2. Doncaster, 3. Longhedge, 4. Inverurie, 5. Darlington, 6. Earlestown, 7. Horwich, 8. St Rollox, 9. Cowlairs, 10. Eastleigh, 11. Wolverhampton, 12. Derby, 13. Oswestry, 14. Ashford, 15. Brighton, 16. Lancing, 17. Stratford, 18. Wolverton, 19. Caerphilly, 20. Gorton. **Picture:** 1982.

Section 12, Stations: True or False. 1. False, 2. False, 3. True, 4. True, 5. True, 6. True, 7. False, 8. False, 9. True, 10. True, 11. False, 12. True, 13. True, 14. False, 15. False, 16. False, 17. True, 18. False, 19. True, 20. False. **Picture:** Boston-Skegness.

Section 13, True or False. 1. True, 2. False — 47500, 3. False — Nene Valley Railway, 4. False — Class 309, 5. True, 6. False — 733, 7. False — 1500-2000hp, 8. True, 9. False — XP64, 10. False — *Voice of the North*, 11. False — Kylchap, 12. True, 13. False — demolished, 14. False — Rail express systems, 15. True. **Picture:** False — they are modified Class 307s.

Section 14, True or False. 1. True, 2. True, 3. True, 4. False — power unit, 5. False — Nimbus, 6. False — River Thames, London, 7. True, 8. False — Swallow, 9. True, 10. False — R.A. Riddles, 11. False — 999, 12. True, 13. False — 'We're getting there', 14. False — V4, 15. False — Sir George Mortimer Pullman. **Picture:** False — it was Greece.

Section 15, Stations. 1. Great Western, 2. Lancashire & Yorkshire, 3. London & South Western, 4. Midland, 5. South Eastern & Chatham, 6. North British, 7. London & North Western, 8. North Eastern, 9. Highland, 10. Great Northern, 11. Midland, 12. Great Northern, 13. London & North Western, 14. Lancashire & Yorkshire, 15. South Eastern and Chatham, 16. Great Central, 17. Great Eastern, 18. Caledonian, 19. London & South Western, 20. North Eastern. **Picture:** The main line station is also used by Manchester Metrolink services, hence the darker signs.

Section 16, Stations. 1. Glasgow, 2. Birmingham, 3. Glasgow, 4. London, 5. London, 6. Birmingham, 7. Glasgow, 8. London, 9. Birmingham, 10. London, 11. Manchester, 12. Manchester, 13. Glasgow, 14. Birmingham, 15. Manchester, 16. Birmingham, 17. Manchester, 18. London, 19. Glasgow, 20. Manchester. **Picture:** Brading, Isle of Wight.

Section 17, Structures. 1. Cantilever, 2. Concrete, 3. 1879, 4. Sir Thomas Bouch, 5. Norwich, 6. Barmouth Bridge, 7. Belah Viaduct, 8. Britannia Tubular Bridge, 9.

London-Brighton, 10. The Royal Border Bridge between Berwick and Tweed-mouth, 11. Severn Valley Railway, 12. It had been struck by a barge in 1960 and damaged, 13. Midland Railway, 14. Welwyn, 15. I.K. Brunel. **Picture:** Tyne & Wear Metro.

Section 18, Structures. 1. Clayton Tunnel, 2. 33 miles 809 yards (53.85 km), 3. 1874, 4. Settle & Carlisle Line, 5. Cowburn Tunnel, 875 ft below the surface at deepest point, 6. Glasgow, 7. 1986, 8. Northern, 9. Tonbridge-Hastings, 10. Llan-gollen Railway, 11. Grantham, 12. 1981, 13. Carlisle-Edinburgh 'Waverley' route, 14. Kings Cross, 15. True. **Picture:** Ryde Esplanade Tunnel, Isle of Wight.

Section 19, Tunnels. 1. Clayton Tunnel, 2. Sapperton Tunnel, 3. Rainbow Hill Tunnel, 4. Whiteball Tunnel, 5. Box Tunnel, 6. Mickleham Tunnel, 7. Sharpthorne Tunnel, 8. Warren Hill Tunnel, 9. Sharnbrook Tunnel, 10. Cowburn Tunnel, 11. Peascliffe Tunnel, 12. Stoke Tunnel, 13. Totley Tunnel, 14. Clarborough Tunnel, 15. Standedge Tunnel. **Picture:** Gasworks Tunnel.

Section 20, Tunnels. 1. Severn Tunnel, 2. Bramhope Tunnel, 3. Blea Moor Tunnel, 4. Drumlanrig Tunnel, 5. Knightswood Tunnel, 6. Somerton Tunnel, 7. Buck-horn Weston Tunnel, 8. Buriton Tunnel, 9. Rise Hill Tunnel, 10. Stainforth Tunnel, 11. Wymington Tunnel, 12. Somerton Tunnel, 13. Greenway Tunnel, 14. Foley Park Tunnel, 15. Wallers Ash Tunnel. **Picture:** Great Central Railway.

Section 21, Stations. 1. Central, Main Line. 2. Docks, Island. 3. Midland, St John's. 4. Oriel Road, New Strand. 5. Forster Square, Exchange. 6. Temple Meads, Parkway. 7. North, South. 8. North, South. 9. Central, Sunnyside. 10. South, West. 11. Central, East. 12. Chase, Town. 13. East, West. 14. High, Gra-hamston. 15. Central, Lea Road. **Picture:** Bradford Forster Square.

Section 22, Summits. 1. Dainton Summit, 2. Whiteball Summit, 3. County March Summit, 4. Ravens Rock Summit, 5. Slochd Summit, 6. Whistlefield Summit, 7. Druimachdar Summit, 8. Cobbinshaw Summit, 9. Beattock Summit, 10. Pinmore Summit, 11. Ais Gill Summit, 12. Shap Summit, 13. Copy Pit Summit, 14. Stand-edge Summit, 15. Talerddig Summit. **Picture:** Rose Grove.

Section 23, On The Line. 1. 393, 2. Swansea-Bridgend, 3. Crewe, 4. Cambridge-St Ives, 5. Shrewsbury, 6. Edinburgh-Carlisle 'Waverley Route', 7. East Suffolk Line, 8. Wick and Thurso, 9. Southall, 10. Bristol, 11. South Yokrshire Supertram, 12. Penzance, 13. Rosslare, 14. Coventry, 15. Knottingley. **Picture:** Loughbor-ough (Midland).

Section 24, On The Line. 1. Salisbury, 2. Glasgow Central, 3. March, 4. 1350ft, 5. Milk, 6. West Somerset, 7. Dagenham, East London, 8. Dartmouth, 9. St. Erth-St. Ives, 10. Birmingham, 11. East Grinstead, 12. Twyford, 13. Nottingham-Mans-field, 14. Doncaster, 15. Blackpool. **Picture:** Old Oak Common.

Section 25, Steam Technology. 1. 2-8-0, 2. Firebox, 3. Coupling, 4. Between the frames, 5. Mixed traffic, 6. Footplate, 7. Chimney, 8. Class 9F 2-10-0s, 9. Forces water into the boiler, 10. Wheel arrangement configuration, 11. Regulator, 12. In the firebox, 13. British, 14. Compounding, 15. Water troughs. **Picture:** Caprotti.

Section 26, Steam Technology. 1. Bulleid-design streamlined locomotive, 2. Raised lip on front of chimney, 3. Wartime German-designed 2-10-0 locomotives, 4. Front end ornamentation between the boiler and frames, 5. The front end door in the streamlining, 6. When flames and high pressure gases are forced back through the firebox door, 7. Feed-water heating equipment for locomotive boilers, 8. A powerful exhaust, 9. Uses steam to force water into the boiler, 10. Overheated axle journal or bearing caused by poor lubrication, 11. Streamlined casing removed, 12. 2-12-0, 13. Red hot cinders thrown from a loco's chimney, 14. SE&CR 4-4-0, 15. Smoke deflectors. **Picture:** Steel.

Section 27, Steam Technology. 1. Wheels, 2. Boiler, 3. Boiler, 4. Wheels, 5. Cab, 6. Boiler, 7. Boiler, 8. Cab, 9. Cab, 10. Boiler, 11. Cab, 12. Wheels, 13. Boiler, 14. Cab, 15. Wheels. **Picture:** Austria.

Section 28, Modern Technology. 1. Electric, 2. Collect electric current from a third rail, 3. Mechanical, 4. Eight, 5. 25 kV ac, 6. Driver's Safety Device, 7. 3,300, 8. Shut off current while electric locomotive is still running, 9. Early-build Class 31 locomotive without headcodes, 10. Alternator, 11. Steam-heat boilers, 12. Traction motors, 13. False, 14. Electric, 15. Bogies. **Picture:** Changeover from overhead to third-rail operation.

Section 29, Modern Technology. 1. Shunters, 2. Vickers-Armstrong, Barrow, 3. Class 03s, 4. Class 33/1, 5. Blue Star, 6. Class 91 (140 mph), 7. Power unit, 8. Picking up electric current, 9. LDA, 10. Transmission, 11. Paxman Valenta, 12. A1A-A1A, 13. 'Gatwick Express' Class 73/2s, 14. Four, 15. Water. **Picture:** La Grange, Chicago.

Section 30, Modern Technology. 1. Body, 2. Cab, 3. Power equipment, 4. Cab, 5. Body, 6. Body, 7. Cab, 8. Power equipment, 9. Power equipment, 10. Body, 11. Cab, 12. Power equipment, 13. Body, 14. Cab, 15. Power equipment. **Picture:** Electro-pneumatic.

Section 31, Abbreviations. 1. Cockermouth, Keswick & Penrith Railway, 2. Cheshire Lines Committee, 3. Colne Valley & Halstead Railway, 4. Furness & Midland Joint Railway, 5. Great Northern & Great Eastern, 6. Great North of Scotland Railway, 7. Glasgow & South Western Railway, 8. London, Brighton & South Coast Railway, 9. London & North Western Railway, 10. London, Tilbury and Southend Railway, 11. Midland & Great Northern Joint Committee, 12. Manchester, Sheffield & Lincolnshire Railway, 13. Midland & South Western Junction Railway, 14. Neath & Brecon Railway, 15. North British Railway, 16. North Staffordshire Railway, 17. Plymouth, Devonport & South Western Junction Railway, 18. South Eastern & Chatham Railway, 19. Taff Vale Railway, 20. Weston, Cleveland & Portishead Railway. **Picture:** Marylebone, Great Central Railway.

Section 32, Abbreviations. 1. Advanced Passenger Train, 2. All Purpose Ticket Issuing System, 3. Component Exchange Maintenance, 4. Continuous Welded Rail, 5. Electro-Pneumatic Brake, 6. Electric Train Heating, 7. Flashing Rear End Device, 8. High Speed Train, 9. Merry-go-round, 10. Overhead Line, 11. Paved Concrete Track, 12. Public Service Obligation, 13. Radio Electronic Token Block, 14. Solid State Interlocking, 15. Time Division Multiplex, 16. Train Engineering Service Company, 17. Total Operations Processing System, 18. Train Operation Unit, 19.

Temporary Speed Restriction, 20. Underground Ticketing System. **Picture:** London & South East.

Section 33, Multiple Unit Codes. 1 Driving Motor Brake Second, 2. Trailer Composite with Lavatory, 3. Trailer First (Corridor), 4. Driving Trailer Brake Second, 5. Driving Motor Brake Composite, 6. Trailer Brake First (Corridor) with Lavatory, 7. Trailer Second, 8. Trailer Composite, 9. Trailer Second Miniature Buffet with Lavatory, 10. Driving Trailer Brake Second, 11. Battery Driving Motor Composite Open with Lavatory, 12. Trailer Second Open with Lavatory, 13. Motor Brake Second Open, 14. Motor Parcels and Mail Van, 15. Driving Motor Second Open, 16. Driving Trailer Second Open, 17. Driving Motor Parcels Van, 18. Motor Second Open, 19. Trailer First Open with Lavatory and Handbrake, 20. Battery Driving Motor. **Picture:** Metropolitan-Cammell.

Section 34, Coaching Stock Codes. 1. Open Brake First, 2. Gangwayed Full Brake, 3. Brake Post Office Stowage Van, 4. Corridor Brake Second, 5. Corridor Composite, 6. Driving Open Brake Second, 7. Driving Brake Van, 8. First Open, 9. General Utility Van, 10. Lounge First, 11. Post Office Sorting Van, 12. Restaurant Buffet, 13. Restaurant Buffet First Modular, 14. Kitchen Car, 15. Miniature Buffet Car with Trolley, 16. Corridor Second, 17. Sleeping Car with Pantry, 18. Trailer Guard's Standard, 19. Trailer Standard, 20. Tourist Second Open with Disabled Access. **Picture:** Eleven.

Section 35, GWR. 1. 171, 2. 1923-50, 3. 7037 *Swindon,* 4. G.J. Churchward, 5. *Viscount Portal,* 6. 111 *Viscount Churchill,* 7. 16, 8. 4073 *Caerphilly Castle,* 9. 7013 *Bristol Castle,* 10. 5017 *The Gloucestershire Regiment 28th 61st,* 11. No. 5000 *Launceston Castle,* 12. March 1950, 13. Australia, 14. Four, 15. Tyseley. **Picture:** Paddington, 1965.

Section 36, GWR. 1. 1927, 2. 30, 3. Baltimore & Ohio Railroad, 4. Four, 5. Collett, 6. 1962, 7. 6014 *King Henry VII,* 8. 6023 and 6024, 9. Great Western Society, Didcot, 10. Double Red, 11. True, 12. 6028 *King George VI* and 6029 *King Edward VIII,* 13. 6018 *King Henry VI,* 14. 8P, 15. Buckinghamshire Railway Centre. **Picture:** Bulmers of Hereford.

Section 37 GWR. 1. 4300 Class 2-6-0s, 2. 1930, 3. C.B. Collett, 4. 4900 *Saint Martin,* 5. Great Western Society, Didcot, 6. Twelve, 1938-50, 7. F.W. Hawksworth, 8. 4911 *Bowden Hall,* 9. 1965, 10. *County of Middlesex,* 11. 6MT, 12. Cambrian, 13. None, 14. 4942 *Maindy Hall,* 15. 7808 *Cookham Manor.* **Picture:** 5MT.

Section 38, GWR. 1. *La France,* 2. *North Star,* 3. Nine, 4. 2-6-0, 5. 167, 1903-42, 6. 'Castles', 7. 2818, 8. 3440 and 3717, 9. 'Dean Goods', 10. 'Dukedog', 11. 4300, 12. 100, 13. 4003 *Lode Star,* 14. 48xx, 15. 2999. **Picture:** Eight.

Section 39, GWR. 1. Prairies, 2. Hawksworth 9400 Class, 3. London Transport, 4. Newcastle (Robert Stephenson & Hawthorn), 5. 1949, 6. 1401, 7. 7200 Class, 8. 8F, 9. Avonside Engine Co., 10. South Wales, 11. 4588, 12. 6400 Class, 13. Inverness (1646/9), 14. 1501, 15. 863. **Picture:** 48xx.

Section 40, GWR. 1. Hurry Riches, 2. *Hercules,* 3. '89' Class, 4. *Edward Thomas,* Talyllyn Railway, 5. Kitson, 6. *Shannon,* 7. Port Talbot Railway, 8. Three, 9. 0-6-2T, 10. Welshpool & Llanfair, 11. Burry Port & Gwendraeth Valley

Railway, 12. Weston, Clevedon & Portishead, 13. *Margaret*, 14. Corris, 15. 1340 *Trojan*, Didcot. **Picture:** Davies & Metcalfe, 1902.

Section 41, SR. 1. 21C1, 2. *Channel Packet*, 3. Ten (35021-30), 4. 6ft 2in, 5. Eastleigh, 6. Southern, 7. BFB (Bulleid-Firth-Brown), 8. R.G. Jarvis, 9. 35018 *British India Line*, 1956, 10. Walschaerts, 11. 1964, 12. Eleven, 13. 35005 *Canadian Pacific*, 14. Longmoor, 15. 35029 *Ellerman Lines*. **Picture:** Carlisle Citadel.

Section 42, SR. 1. 110, 2. 1945, 3. 4-6-2, 4. Brighton, 5. 34001-48/91-108, 6. 7P5F, 7. *Fighter Command*,8. 34004-6, 9. 21C149, 10. 60, 11. 34104 *Bere Alston*, 12. July 1967, 13. 34023 *Blackmore Vale*, 14. January 1965, 15. 34092 *City of Wells*. **Picture:** *Clovelly* is a 'West Country'.

Section 43, SR. 1. Eastleigh, 1926-9, 2. 16, 3. Four, 4. 859 *Lord Hood*, 5. Steamtown Carnforth, 6. V, 7. 1930, 8. *Uppingham, Bradfield*, 9. 30926 *Repton*, 10. Conversion into snowploughs, 11. Urie and Maunsell, 12. 1918, 13. 73 — 448-57, 736-55, 763-806, 14. 1962, 15. No. 453. **Picture:** Cannon Street.

Section 44, SR. 1. Southampton Docks, 2. 800 *River Cray*, 3. 0-8-0T, 4. Eight, 5. 30950-7, 6. 1931, 7. 1964, 8. Three, 9. Central and St. David's, 10. Metropolitan Railway, 11. O.V.S. Bulleid, 12. One, 13. 36001 upwards, 14. Kent & East Sussex Railway, 15. Class K1. **Picture:** Class N1.

Section 45, SR. 1. Q1, 2. C1-C40, 3. 2-6-4T, 4. 530-49, 5. 4F, 6. 32039 *Hartland Point*, 7. Class L1, 8. Six, 9. True, 10. Woolwich Arsenal, 11. Twenty, 790-809, 12. *River Torridge*, 13. 30499 and 30506, 14. 30825, 15. S15 30841. **Picture:** Bluebell Railway.

Section 46, SR. 1. Wenford Bridge, Cornwall, 2. *Birch Grove*, 3. 02, 4. True, 5. 'Paddleboxes', 6. Class P, 323, 7. 4-6-4T, 8. 1872, 9. Berlin, 10. 1905, 11. Class 0415, 12. *Remembrance*, 13. Two, 30053 and 30245, 14. *Burgundy*, 15. Class B4 0-4-0T, **Picture:** LSWR (No. 24), LB&SCR (No. 2).

Section 47 LMS. 1 6200, 2. Crewe, 1933, 3. 1962, 4. 6205 *Princess Victoria*, 5. 46202 *Princess Anne*, 6. Destroyed in 1952 Harrow disaster, 7. Midland Railway Centre, 8. 6229, 9. 6256, Sir William Stanier, 10. 46257, entered service after Nationalisation, 11. Southern, 12. 1964, 13. Sir Billy Butlin, 14. *City of Leeds*, 15. Yes. **Picture:** Swindon.

Section 48, LMS. 1. 1927, 2. 71, 3. North British Locomotive Company, Glasgow, 4. Three, 5. 6170 *British Legion*, 6. 7P, 7. 46106, 8. 46152, 9. Two, 5735/6, 10. 45637 *Windward Isles*, 11. *Britannia*, 12. Leeds Holbeck, 13. Double chimney, 14. 45690 (5690) *Leander*, 15. East Lancashire Railway. **Picture:** *Sierra Leone*.

Section 49, LMS. 1. 44781, 2. 44871 and 45110, 3. 5000, Crewe Works, 4. 17 years, 1934-51, 5. 842, 6. Stephenson link motion, 7. 44658, 8. Five, 9. 45156 *Ayrshire Yeomanry*, 10. Carnforth, Lostock Hall, Rose Grove, 11. 1935, 12. Doncaster, 13. True, 14. 1957, 15. 666. **Picture:** 44765.

Section 50, LMS. 1. Somerset & Dorset, 2. Severn Valley Railway, 3. 'Prince of Wales' 4-6-0, 4. 0-8-0, 49500-674, 5. 'Crab' 2-6-0, 6. Coal, 7. 2-6-6-2, 8. 40, 9. 'Claughtons', 10. 52, 11. Class 8F 2-8-0, 12. 1925, 13. Reidinger, 14. True, 15. 4027. **Picture:** 'Flying Pig'.

Section 51, LMS. 1. 2-6-2T, 2. 40001, 3. London, Tilbury & Southend, 4. 47009, 5. 'Jinty', 6. False — it was Brighton, 7. Charles Fairbairn, 8. *The Prince*, 9. Northern Ireland, 10. Lancashire & Yorkshire Railway, 11. 42073 and 42085, 12. Class 2P 0-4-4Ts, 13. Class 2P, 14. 130, 15. 0-8-4T. **Picture:** H.G. Ivatt.

Section 52, LMS. 1. Staveley Ironworks, 2. Eleven, 3. 'Pugs', 4. Whitelegg, 5. Great Central 2-8-0, ex-ROD, 6. 0-10-0, 7. Lickey Incline, 8. 1000, 9. North London Railway, 10. Glasgow & South Western, 11. 54398 *Ben Alder*, 12. Glasgow Transport Museum, 13. North Staffordshire, 14. 'River' 4-6-0s, 15. 4-4-0. **Picture:** North London Railway.

Section 53, LNER. 1. 1935, 2. 4468 Mallard, 3. 60022, 4. July 3 1938, near Grantham, 5. 35, 6. 4469, 7. *Sir Ralph Wedgwood*, 8. *William Whitelaw*, 9. False. It was his 100th, 10. Silver grey, 11. 2509 *Silver Link*, 12. King's Cross, 13. Scottish, 14. 60009, 15. 60008 and 60010. **Picture:** 1938.

Section 54, LNER. 1. A1, 2. 4472 *Flying Scotsman*, 3. Great Northern Railway, 4. German-type smoke deflectors, 5. *Prince Palatine*, 6. Forty, 7. Edward Thompson, 8. 2-8-2 (Class P2), 9. Polmadie, 10. 60532 *Blue Peter*, 11. 4470 *Great Northern*, 12. Doncaster and Darlington, 49, 13. Five, 14. 60114 *W.P. Allen*, 15. 60163 *Tornado*. **Picture:** Loughborough (Great Central Railway).

Section 55, LNER. 1. Sir Nigel Gresley, 2. Fast goods service, 3. 60800-983, 4. True, 5. 7P6F, 6. Antelope, 7. 61057, 8. 61306 *Mayflower,* 9. Stationary boilers, 10. 61264, 11. North of Scotland, 12. Named after football clubs, 13. *East Anglian* and *City of London*, 14. Class B2, 15. 100A. **Picture:** It is the sole-surviving inside-cylindered 4-6-0.

Section 56, LNER. 1. K5, 2. West Highland Line, 3. Two, 4. James Holden, 5. Great Central, 6. Railway Operating Department (Royal Engineers), 7. Q6 and Q7, 8. Class J11, 9. First World War, 10. C, 11. North East, 12. *Glen Douglas*, 13. 70, 14. D49, 15. 10000. **Picture:** Class K3.

Section 57, LNER. 1. J94, 2. 2-6-4T, 3. 100, 4. Class J72, 5. 67600-91, 6. Cromford & High Peak Line, 7. Class J50, 8. Sentinel, 9. Class A8, 10. False, 11. Moorgate, 12. Three, 13. 1964, 14. *Joem,* 15. Great Central Railway, Loughborough, **Picture:** LNER (not GER), 69621.

Section 58, LNER 1. Class Y5, 2. North British, 3. S, 4. 69910-22, Class T1, 5. Class J88, 6. USA (Sacramento), 7. 68619, 8. 2-2-4T, 9. *Aerolite*, 10. Manning Wardle, 11. W.P. Reid, 12. No, 13. 2-4-2T, 14. True, 15. H.A. Ivatt. **Picture:** Sharp Stewart.

Section 59, BR. 1. 1951, 2. Eastern, 3. Carlisle Kingmoor, 4. Bressingham, Norfolk, 5. 70004/9/14, 6. 70047, 7. 70001 *Lord Hurcomb*, 8. Two, 9. Westinghouse air pumps, 10. 8P, 11. Ten (72000-9), 12. Fifteen, 13. Southern, 14. Darlington Works, 15. 72008 *Clan MacLeod*. **Picture:** *William Shakespeare*.

Section 60, BR. 1. 172, 2. Derby and Doncaster, 3. 1951, 4. 73050-2, 5. Ex-SR 'King Arthurs', 6. 73080-9, 73110-9, 7. Caprotti, 8. 73129, 9. 75000-79, 10. 90 (75000-89), 11. Scottish and North Eastern, 12. August 1968, 13. Double chimney, 14. *The Green Knight*, 15. Brighton. **Picture:** 1951-57.

Section 61, BR. 1. 1952, 2. LMS 43000 series, 3. London Midland, 4. Doncaster, 5. 76017, 6. 82000 Class, 7. BR8, 8. Swindon, 9. 77014, 10. Five, 11. 78000-64, 12. Western, 13. True, 14. 78018, 15. KWVR. **Picture:** 76077, Gloucestershire Warwickshire Railway.

Section 62, BR. 1. 1954, 2. Swindon and Crewe, 3. March 1960, 4. 92220, 5. Three (92165-7), 6. David Shepherd, 7. Giesl ejector, 8. Carnforth, 9. 92178, 10. 92240, 11. Ten (92020-9), 12. One, 13. 5ft 0in, 14. Consett, 15. 92134. **Picture:** Western Region.

Section 63, BR. 1. 80010, 2. London, Tilbury & Southend, 3. 80154, 4. 80103, 5. Eastfield, 6. 82000, 7. 63, 8. 45, 9. 1964, 10. Waterloo ECS pilots, 11. Crewe and Darlington, 12. 41200-329, 13. Isle of Wight, 14. True, 15. 84030. **Picture:** North Yorkshire Moors Railway.

Section 64, Diesel Shunters. 1. Dock shunting, 2. Reading Signal Works, 3. D2400-9, 4. 13000, 5. Swindon Works, 1957, 6. Two, 7. 08888, 8. 13079 (08064), 9. Hydraulic, 10. D2953, 11. Brush Traction, 12. LMS, 13. Sheffield, 14. Chesterton Junction (Cambridge), 15. Class 02. **Picture:** Isle of Wight.

Section 65, Class 20. 1. 1957, 2. It was the first Modernisation Plan locomotive delivered, 3. Vulcan Foundry, 4. 20, 5. Dual braking, fitting of slow speed control equipment, 6. 20901-6, 7. Weedkilling trains, 8. Channel Tunnel, 9. 20189, 10. Traction, 11. 20050, 12. D8128 (20128), 13. France, 14. British Nuclear Fuels, 15. 20301-5. **Picture:** London Underground.

Section 66, Classes 26-27. 1 Southern, 2. 1160hp, 3. For use on LT Widened Lines, 4. Iron ore trains, 5. Llangollen Railway, 6. Rats, 7. D7660, 8. Three, 9. 25322 *Tamworth Castle*, 10. 1986, 11. Hornsey, 12. Smethwick (Birmingham), 13. Slow-speed equipment, 14. Edinburgh-Glasgow, 15. Bo'ness. **Picture:** Scottish, Midland, North Eastern.

Section 67, Class 31. 1 November 1957, 2. A1A-A1A, 3. 'Toffee Apples', 4. Stratford, 5. Bronze Gold, 6. Mirrlees, 1250 bhp, 7. D5511, 8. D5835, 9. 31150, October 1975, 10. Cricklewood, 11. East Lancashire Railway, 12. 69, 13. 31296 *Amlwch Freighter*, 14. *Boadicea*, 15. 97204. **Picture:** Doncaster.

Section 68, Class 33. 1. 98, 2. Generator and traction motors, 3. Eastleigh, 4. D6502, 5. 33008, 6 19, 7. Class 34, 8. Tonbridge-Hastings, 9. Slow-speed control, 10. 33027 and 33056, 11.33056 and 33202, 12. Eight, 13. 1550, 14. D6580 (33119), 15. 33109 and 33116. **Picture:** 4-TC.

Section 69, Class 35. 1. 101, 2. Western, 3. D7000-D7100, 4. Type 3, 5. Beyer Peacock, Manchester, 6. Maybach MD870, 7. Hydraulic Mekydro transmission, 8. Yellow Triangle, 9. True, 10. 1971, 11. Lickey Incline, 12. D7076/96, 13. Old Dalby, 14. West Somerset Railway, 15. D7029. **Picture:** No. D7017 on the West Somerset Railway.

Section 70, Class 37 1. D6700, 2. 37350, 3. Co-Co, 4. D6983, 5. 31, 6. Crewe, 7. 119, 8. Eastern, 9. D6881/2, 10. Alternator, 11. Class 37/6, 12. Mirrlees MB275T and Ruston RK270T, 13. D6703/4/7, 14. White 'Police' livery, 15. 37425 Sir *Robert McAlpine/Concrete Bob*. **Picture:** D6603, 37303.

Section 71, Class 40. 1. Stratford, Hornsey, 2. 1958, 3. Whistlers, 4. D322, 5. 40122, 6. Toton, 7. D345 (40145), 8. East Lancashire Railway, Bury, 9. 2000, 10. D326, 11. 125, 12. Crewe, 13. One, D255 (for a short time only), 14. Robert Stephenson & Hawthorn, Darlington, 15. *Media*. **Picture:** 25, D210-25 and D227-35.

Section 72, Classes 41-43. 1. North British Locomotive Company, 2. MAN, 3. Landore, 4. Two, D600/2, 5. D601 *Ark Royal*, 6. *Sir Brian Robertson*, 7. *Despatch*, 8. Ship's crest, 9. December 1972, 10. D818 *Glory*, 11. D830 *Majestic*, 12. Type 4, 13. 33, 14. 1969, 15. None. **Picture:** D821 *Greyhound*.

Section 73, Classes 44-46. 1. *Scafell Pike*, 2. Switzerland, 3. D2 *Helvellyn*, 4. D8 *Schiehallion*, 5. Toton, 6. 1Co-Co1, 7. Five (D11-15), 8. 1963 (D57), 9. *Lytham St Annes*, 10. D100, 11. 56, 12. Brush, 13. *Ixion*, 14. Swindon, 15. Doncaster Works, 1984. **Picture:** 97403.

Section 74, Class 47. 1. Brush, Loughborough, 2. Crewe, 3. 512, 4. 12LDA28C, 5. Sulzer 2650hp 'V' engine, 6. 47299 (47216), 7. 47054 *Xancidae*, 8. Bridgend, 9. D1733, 10. Midland Railway Centre, 11. 17, 12. Crewe, 13. 95mph, 14. *Merddin Emrys*, 15. D1628/47046/47601/47901. **Picture:** None.

Section 75, Class 50. 1. 50, 2. 1967/68, 3. DP2, 4. None, 5. Orange Square, 6. 50007 *Sir Edward Elgar*, 7. *Hercules*, 8. 50033 *Glorious*, 9. 50041 *Bulwark*, 10 Crewe Diesel, 11. D400, October 1972, 12. Doncaster, 13. Re-geared bogies, 14. 100mph, 15. 50021 *Rodney*. **Picture:** Waterloo-Exeter, National Railway Museum.

Section 76, Class 52. 1. Desert sand, 2. Maroon, 3. 2700, 4. Laira, 5. Laira (again), 6. D1023, 7. 44, 8. D1019 *Western Challenger*, 9. D1013 and D1023, 10. D1029 *Western Legionaire*, 11. Swindon, 12. 1973, 13. D1062 *Western Courier*, 14. Stone trains, 15. 1200 Falcon. **Picture:** When new, golden ochre livery.

Section 77, Class 55. 1. Finsbury Park, Gateshead and Haymarket, 2. 99 tons, 3. 55020 *Nimbus*, 4. 1980, 5. D9002 (55002), 6. 18, 7. White cab surrounds, 8. 55001 and 55007, 9. 55008 and 55021, 10. Six, 11. 3300hp, 12. Eight, 13. January 2 1982, 14. 55010 *King's Own Scottish Borderer*, 15. 55015 *Tulyar*. **Picture:** Flashing headlight.

Section 78, Classes 56-60. 1. Romania, 2. 56031, 3. 56036, 4. Crewe, 5. 56042, September 1991, 6. 50, 7. Doncaster, 1983-87, 8. None, 9. 58050, 10. 1986, 11. 15, 12. 3,300, 13. Brush Traction, 14. Co-Co, 15. 60mph. **Picture:** Leicestershire.

Section 79 Classes 71-77. 1. E5000, 2. 'Gatwick Express', 3. 600hp, 4. 73201 (73142) Broadlands, 5. 73801, 6. Transrail blue, 7. O.V.S. Bulleid, 8. Birkenhead, 9. Ten, Crewe Works, 10. Netherlands, 11. Reddish, 12. The line closed, 13. Seven, 14. Lined black, 15. 1501 (27003) *Diana*. **Picture:** *Brighton Evening Argus*.

Section 80, Classes 81-92. 1. November 1959, 2. E3001, 81001, 3. Ten, 4. Stepless voltage control, 5. North British, Glasgow, 6. E3061 (85006/85101), 7. All withdrawn after collisions, 8. Three, 86101-3, 9. Class 86/6, 10. *Stephenson* and *Royal Scot*, 11. Co-Co, 12. 90016-20, 13. 140mph, 14. 6,090, 15. Railfreight Distribution, European Passenger Services, SNCF. **Picture:** *Northampton Town*.

Section 81, LNER. 1. K, 2. D, 3. O, 4. G, 5. R, 6. E, 7. L, 8. Q, 9. A, 10. I, 11. P, 12. F, 13. M, 14. T, 15. B, 16. N, 17. H, 18. J, 19. S, 20. C. **Picture:** Class D30 No. 62426.

Section 82, LMS. 1. C, 2. E, 3. O, 5. R, 6. T, 7. D, 8. L, 9. Q, 10. J, 11. M, 12. A, 13. P, 14. N, 15. I, 16. F, 17. K, 18. B, 19. S, 20. G. **Picture:** Coventry.

Section 83, SR. 1. C, 2. G, 3. B, 4. J, 5. P, 6. F, 7. N, 8. S, 9. A, 10. O, 11. T, 12. Q, 13. K, 14. H, 15. R, 16. E, 17. L, 18. I, 19. M, 20. D. **Picture:** 35001.

Section 84, GWR. 1. S, 2. A, 3. D, 4. I, 5. K, 6. N, 7. C, 8. H, 9. Q, 10. T, 11. L, 12. B, 13. R, 14. E, 15. O, 16. J, 17. M, 18. F, 19. G, 20. P. **Picture:** 5933.

Section 85, BR. 1. D, 2. O, 3. K, 4. I, 5. Q, 6. E, 7. P, 8. L, 9. H, 10. B, 11. C, 12. R, 13. J, 14. N, 15. T, 16. F, 17. S, 18. M, 19. G, 20. A. **Picture:** 87004.

Section 86, Diesel Locomotives. 1. D, 2. H, 3. N, 4. A, 5. T, 6. R, 7. J, 8. E, 9. L, 10. O, 11. G, 12. S, 13. P, 14. F, 15. I, 16. B, 17. Q, 18. K, 19. M, 20. C. **Picture:** 60001.

Section 87, Electric Locomotives. 1. F, 2. L, 3. J, 4. P, 5. G, 6. T, 7. H, 8. M, 9. R, 10. A, 11. C, 12. O, 13. D, 14. K, 15. B, 16. N, 17. E, 18. S, 19. I, 20. Q. **Picture:** Ian Allan.

Section 88, Foreign Railways. 1. Inchicore, 2. Larne, 3. Belfast Central and Dublin Connolly, 4. DART, 5. General Motors, 6. Main station, 7. 15 kV ac, 8. 1977, 9. White and red, 10. Small diesel shunter, 11. CP, 12. Lisbon, 13. 5ft 6in (1668 mm), 14. Barreiro, 15. False — 1800 Class. **Picture:** France.

Section 89, Foreign Railways. 1. Four, 2. Expresszug, 3. E, 4. 150, 5. Sweden, 6. Train à Grand Vitesse, 7. Gare du Lyon, 8. Mulhouse 9. Y, 10. Class 62000, 11. Nederlandse Spoorwegen, 12. True, 13. France, 14. 1200 Class, 15. The Camel. **Picture:** BB 17000.

Section 90, Foreign Railways. 1. SNCB (French), NMBS (Flemish), 2. False — the Belgian locomotives are Belgian-built, 3. Mechelen and Salzinnes, 4. Class 11, 5. Yellow and green, 6. Rede Nacional de los Ferrocarriles Españoles, 7. 1676mm, 1435mm, and 1000mm, 8. TALGO, 9. Algeciras (near Gibraltar), 10. 1992, 11. SBB, CFF and FFS, 12. Lausanne, Luzern and Zürich, 13. Re 4/4 1, 14. Berne-Lötschberg-Simplon Railway, 15. Winterthur. **Picture:** Portugal, Ten.

Section 91, Pictures. A. Portugal (Tunes), B. France (Thionville), C. Germany (Köln), D. Spain (Teulada).

Section 92, Pictures. A. Switzerland (Basel). B. Italy (Vipiteno), C. Austria (Innsbruck), D. Belgium (Antwerpen).

Section 93, Preservation. 1. Oxenhope, 2. Cheddleton, 3. Colonel Holman Stephens, 4. London, Brighton & South Coast Railway, 5. Bo'ness, 6. Birmingham Museum of Science & Industry, 7. Embsay, 8. Vale of Rheidol Railway, 9. East Somerset Railway, 10. 18 miles, 11. Haltwhistle-Alston, 12. East Lancashire Railway, 13. Didcot, 14. Midland & Great Northern Joint, 15. South Yorkshire Railway. **Picture:** St. Rollox, 2P.

Section 94, Preservation. 1. Matlock and Buxton, 2. Cheltenham Racecourse, 3. Tyseley, 4. 1976, 5. Isle of Wight Steam Railway, 6. Strathspey Railway, 7. Midland Railway Centre, Butterley, 8. Paignton & Dartmouth, 9. Loughborough, 10. Peterborough, 11. Lake Windermere, 12. Swindon & Cricklade Railway, 13. London Transport Museum, Covent Garden, 14. Ashburton, 15. Scunthorpe. **Picture:** Rainhill, Liverpool.

Section 95, Preservation. 1. Southall, 2. Lochty Railway, 3. 15in, 4. Leeds, 5. Sittingbourne & Kelmsley Light Railway, 6. True, 7. False — GWR, 8. Seaton and Colyton, 9. Steamtown Carnforth, 10. Cumbria, 11. 8M, 12. 3494ft, 13. Corfe Castle, 14. Brechin, 15. Hereford. **Picture:** Strathspey Railway, *Schiehallion*.

Section 96, Preserved Locomotives. 1. 'Greyhound', 2. Derwent Valley Railway, 3. 'Coal Tank', 4. Yugoslavia, 5. Waterloo & City, 6. 0-6-0T, 7. Crossley, 8. False — 31018, 9. S160, 10. 45160, 11. Broad Gauge (7ft), 12. *Atlantic Conveyor,* 13. Alan Pegler, 14. A.J. Hill, 15. Cardiff. **Picture:** Glasgow Transport Museum.

Section 97, Preserved Locomotives. 1. *Sovereign,* 2. Steam Locomotive Operators' Association, 3. Midland Railway Centre, 4. D400, 5. Manchester Museum of Science & Technology, 6. Severn Valley Railway, 7. North British, 8. *Tamworth Castle*, 9. Class J17, 10. 7754, 11. *Morayshire,* 12. One, 09002, 13. True, 14. Broad gauge (7ft), 15. 29. **Picture:** Australia, No. 4079 *Pendennis Castle*.

Section 98, Anagrams. 1. Marylebone, 2. Kings Cross, 3. Paddington, 4. London Bridge, 5. Euston, 6. St Pancras, 7. Charing Cross, 8. Waterloo, 9. Victoria, 10. Liverpool Street, 11. Blackfriars, 12. Cannon Street, 13. Fenchurch Street, 14. Moorgate, 15. Kensington Olympia, 16. Farringdon, 17. Clapham Junction, 18. Finsbury Park, 19. Gospel Oak, 20. Old Street. **Picture:** International Coach, Derby (Litchurch Lane) Works.

Section 99, Anagrams. 1. Toton, 2. Old Oak Common, 3. Motherwell, 4. Haymarket, 5. Allerton, 6. Landore, 7. Willesden, 8. Cardiff Canton, 9. Longsight, 10. Knottingley, 11. Bounds Green, 12. Newton Heath, 13. Stewarts Lane, 14. Stratford, 15. Slade Green, 16. Laira, 17. Inverness, 18. Eastleigh, 19. Polmadie, 20. Doncaster. **Picture:** Stewarts Lane.

Section 100, True or False? 1. True, 2. False — Horwich, 3. True, 4. False — Switzerland, 5. True, 6. True, 7. True, 8. False — 10100, 9. False — ICI, 10. True, 11. False — Great North of Scotland Railway, 12. True, 13. True, 14. False — Wolverton did not build any BR locomotives, 15. False — *The Red Knight*. **Picture:** False. It was the Rev Wilbert Awdry.